ANORGANISCHE UND ALLGEMEINE CHEMIE
IN EINZELDARSTELLUNGEN
HERAUSGEGEBEN VON
MARGOT BECKE-GOEHRING

BAND IV

# INORGANIC ADDUCT MOLECULES OF OXO-COMPOUNDS

BY

INGVAR LINDQVIST
UPPSALA / SWEDEN

WITH 18 FIGURES

1963

NEW YORK
ACADEMIC PRESS INC., PUBLISHERS

BERLIN · GÖTTINGEN · HEIDELBERG
SPRINGER-VERLAG

SPRINGER-VERLAG
BERLIN · GÖTTINGEN · HEIDELBERG

*Published in U.S.A. and Canada by*
ACADEMIC PRESS INC., PUBLISHERS
*111 Fifth Avenue, New York 3, New York*



*Library of Congress Catalog Card Number 62–22222*


*Printed in Germany*

## Preface

Chemistry is a subject experiencing very rapid growth. New areas of research are opened and new methods are developed with a speed which must seem impressive. The picture has, however, another side represented by the great number of unsolved or poorly solved problems left behind when a branch of chemistry is no longer fashionable. When three years ago I began to plan this book I felt that the molecular adducts of oxo-compounds constituted just such a field of research, and that they might acquire greater interest if approached from the standpoint of modern chemistry. The developments of the last three years have been such, however, that it can no longer be said that interest is lacking. From that point of view a book on this subject may now seem unnecessary. On the other hand individual contributions to this field have been very scattered, and the essential problems have not always been recognized. It is hoped therefore that this book will help to coordinate work on these compounds and that future investigations will derive some benefit as a result.

For this purpose a systematic treatment is needed and the first and larger part of the book is an attempt to present a fairly complete review of past experimental work. The treatment is not detailed; it is aimed instead at giving the reader a chance to find all the pertinent references. I have tried to make this part readable by giving brief summaries of the present state of experimental knowledge, but the main value lies in the references. Theoretical discussions have been almost completely excluded from this section since such discussions have never tried to correlate *all* the experimental facts. Each reader is thus in a position to make his own interpretation founded on an unbiased presentation of the experimental results. His interpretation will depend, of course upon his understanding of the subject and must therefore be restricted by the often severe limitations of his theoretical knowledge. I feel, however, that chemists should only use theoretical concepts which it is natural for them to apply, and that they should not add to them a more sophisticated treatment which has never been part of their mental work but is instead a mere ornament.

For this reason I have presented the theoretical treatment as a separate part of the book. The presentation here is restricted to thoughts and ideas which have been of definite value to me or have developed naturally during my active work in the field. Part of this section could have been given a more sophisticated treatment without adding anything to the clarity and part of it could probably have been improved by a deeper theoretical knowledge. My experience from lectures and discussions is that the level of complexity chosen is one which is considered useful by a great number of experimental chemists. Even if a more thorough theoretical treatment is later attempted it would probably profit to some extent from the correlation of the large number of facts which has been effected here using this simple approach.

The present book does not give the historical development of the subject. This is not due to any lack of appreciation of the early pioneer work. The reference system used here permits everyone to obtain a historical view by reading selected references in chronological order. While making a final check of the reference list I did this myself and was impressed to see how much the development has been due to a few leading pioneers and also to see to what extent the fashions of chemistry have changed during a century of research.

The greater part of the inspiration for writing this book has come from discussions with my students and in this connection I wish to make particular mention of Drs. BRÄNDÉN, HANSSON, HERMODSSON and ZACKRISSON. It should be made clear that this work is a direct result of the generous support which my investigations have received from the Air Force Office of Scientific Research of the Air Research and Developement Command, United States Air Force, and the Swedish Natural Science Research Council and to them I should like to dedicate this book. I also wish to thank Professor GUNNAR HÄGG who first introduced me to the science of chemistry and from whom I have learnt so many of my basic concepts.

Finally I wish to thank Professor Margot Becke-Goehring and Springer Verlag who encouraged me to write this book, Dr. and Mrs. Allan Brown who helped me with the linguistic problems and the Office staff of the Institute of Chemistry, University of Uppsala, who typed the manuscript and made the drawings.

Uppsala, March 1962 INGVAR LINDQVIST

# Contents

# 1. Introduction

The title of this book needs some qualification. The subject can be defined more exactly as the systematic chemistry of the molecular adducts formed between some inorganic electron pair acceptors (Lewis acids) and oxo-compounds acting as electron pair donors (Lewis bases).

The prefix "oxo" is used to indicate that the compounds contain at least one oxygen atom which is bonded to only *one* other atom. This excludes the class of donor molecules such as water, alcohols, ethers and phenols which only contain oxygen atoms bonded to two other atoms. These form a very large number of adducts which are here only mentioned occasionally for purposes of comparison. They do not offer the same possibilities as the oxo-compounds for substitution with atoms other than carbon.

A Lewis acid is characterized by its electron pair acceptor properties which can generally be attributed to one particular acceptor atom. All types of acceptor atoms are dealt with in this book, but not all the possible acceptor molecules have been covered. The restriction to acceptor molecules in which the acceptor atom is bound to hydrogen or halogen, or to alkyl and aryl groups (with some additional examples of other types) detracts little from the completeness of the treatment.

The main reason for the selection of *molecular adducts* is that in such compounds the lattice energies play a minor role, permitting a more straightforward discussion of the donor-acceptor interaction. The results have a bearing on complex formation in general, however, and comparisons have been made whenever they have been found interesting.

As stated in the Preface, the intention has been to present a more or less organized compilation of the widely scattered literature in this field. Many of the papers which have been quoted concern another research topic, the adducts only being described in connection with, for example, the characterization or isolation of organic donor molecules. The variety of interests underlying the research thus reviewed has complicated the compilation (and probably increased the number of errors and omissions); on the other hand it is possible that the book will be of interest not only to inorganic but also to organic chemists. In any case those working with X-ray crystallography, thermo-chemistry, spectroscopy and theoretical chemistry, all dealing in one way or another with the nature of the chemical bond, will find here a wealth of related compounds, supplying ample opportunity to make those comparisons which are so important as tests of the validity of semi-empirical rules or quantum-mechanical theories.

The chapters on decomposition reactions and catalytic applications have been included for the benefit of the many inorganic chemists who are not familiar with these aspects of adduct molecules. The treatment is by no means complete but is aimed at giving a general impression of the difficulties and possibilities involved in their investigation.

## 2. Conditions for adduct molecule formation

Before beginning the systematic treatment, the conditions for adduct molecule formation will be discussed in a purely formal way. Using the compositions given by chemical analysis, an attempt will be made to predict which of the addition compounds with a given acceptor compound $AB_n$ might be molecular adducts. (The discussion can easily be extended to the more general case of a compound $A_mB_n$.) In the compound $AB_n$, atom A is the less electronegative atom and also the site of the acceptor properties. The compound $AB_n$ can be a discrete *molecule* or it can have an infinite structure in one, two or three dimensions.

It will be shown that in general the formation of an adduct molecule occurs more readily with an acceptor molecule than with a compound having some kind of extended structure. Both cases are encountered, however, and the following discussion is valid for either.

We now assume that a given coordination number can be regarded as characterising a given class of acceptor compounds or, more generally, a given acceptor atom. In most cases it is possible to suggest with some certainty what this *characteristic coordination number* is. It is always higher than the coordination number in the free acceptor compound if this is a molecule, but is often the same as that in the acceptor compound if the latter has an infinite structure. The difficulties encountered in specific cases will be discussed in the next chapter which deals with acceptor compounds; for the present it is sufficient to assume that such a characteristic coordination number is known.

If the donor molecule D contains only one donor atom with only one donor site, such as the oxygen atom in the oxo-compounds, the resultant adduct with the analytical composition $AB_n \cdot pD$ will fall into one of three categories.

The simplest case is that in which $n + p$, i. e. the sum of the number of atoms B and donor molecules D, is equal to the characteristic coordination number of the atom A. An adduct molecule is usually formed in this case, and all adducts with such compositions are included in the systematic treatment. There is, however, one other possibility which must be considered, namely that ions may form by internal exchange of ions and molecules. A typical example is the reaction $B_2H_6 + 2NH_3 = BH_2(NH_3)_2^+ BH_4^-$. The adduct $BH_3 \cdot NH_3$ *can* exist both as a molecular adduct and, according to the preceding formula, as a salt. This has been demonstrated by Parry and his collaborators in a series of elegant experiments (e. g. 1958: 1, 2). Another quite recent suggestion is that $SbCl_5 \cdot CH_3CN$ should instead be formulated $[SbCl_4(CH_3CN)_2]^+SbCl_6^-$. (The present writer has made a slight revision of the formula as originally given (1961: 1) since this appears incomplete.) A specific example of an oxo-compound is $CoX_2 \cdot 3R_2SO$ (p. 10). (See also the chapter on ternary compounds (p. 48) and the treatment of internal exchange of ions and molecules in solution (p. 56).)

In the second category the value of n + p is *smaller* than the characteristic coordination number, and the acceptor atoms must share the B atoms or donor molecules in some way. The extent of such sharing cannot easily be predicted, and compounds of this type are included in the systematic treatment in instances where the formation of a discrete but polymeric molecule is at all possible. A typical example is $TiCl_4 \cdot POCl_3$ (1960: 1), a dimeric molecule with a double chlorine bridge between the titanium atoms; none of the titanium-chlorine bonds in the original $TiCl_4$ molecule are broken (Fig. 9). An example of an infinite structure is given by the adduct $CdCl_2 \cdot 2NH_2CONHCONH_2$ (1960: 7) in which the chlorine bridges extend through the whole crystal, corresponding to an infinite structure in one dimension (Fig. 3).

Polymerization of this type influences the composition of an adduct as though more than one donor atom were effective. Consequently, the possible occurence of such polymerization often complicates predictions regarding adducts formed with donor molecules containing more than one possible donor atom.

The third category of adduct is that in which n + p is *greater* than the characteristic coordination number. In general it can be concluded that in this instance substitution has occurred. No discrete molecules are formed, but complex ions exist in which there is no longer any bonding between the A and B atoms. The latter fact provides an important contradistinction from the first two types of coordination. The classical example of this type of adduct formation is $CoCl_3 + 6\,NH_3 = [Co(NH_3)_6]Cl_3$. Where it is evident that an adduct is of this type, it has been excluded from the systematic treatment. Members of this class constitute the majority of the adducts with water and with ammonia, and they are also encountered among adducts of oxo-compounds, although in this instance they are comparatively less common. A further possibility is provided by the formation of loose adducts and some examples of this class of compounds will be given below (p. 48 and 49).

With the aid of this formal discussion of the conditions for adduct molecule formation it is now possible to select the compounds for systematic treatment without having any preconceived ideas as to the nature of the chemical bonds involved. It is necessary, however, to have a reasonable knowledge of the characteristic coordination numbers, and the possibilities for predicting this quantity will be discussed in the next chapter.

## 3. Characteristic coordination numbers

Knowledge of characteristic coordination numbers is based mainly on collected structural data. The discussion in the preceding chapter demonstrates the importance of defining the possible upper limit for the characteristic coordination number. This minimises the risk of excluding some relevant adducts, which is of greater importance than the risk of inclusion by error of some non-molecular adducts. In the following brief discussion of different classes of acceptor atoms, we will confine ourselves to those atoms which can safely be assumed to belong to one particular class, thus eliminating the need for further comment in the systematic section. Where there is some uncertainty this will be pointed out, so that it will be left to the reader to make a critical evaluation of the compounds included in the systematic section.

**Alkali metals.** The characteristic coordination number for alkali metal ions is six. For lithium, four-fold coordination can also be considered possible. Since the alkali metal ions are only monovalent this means that, as a rule, *five* donor molecules must be added to make possible the formation of a neutral molecule. This, however, would be energetically unfavourable; the molecule would be "overcrowded" with neutral donor molecules (in view of the low positive charge on the metal ions), and the formation of adduct molecules with alkali metal ions can therefore be considered as highly improbable. (The above discussion which relates principally to halides does not apply, however, to large and bulky anions.) For lithium there is the possibility of adding only three donor molecules, and it thus stands a better chance of forming a molecular adduct, but no established examples are known, and the adducts with alkali metal halides are therefore, with a few exceptions, excluded from the systematic treatment. So far the non-existence of adduct molecules has been assumed to arise mainly from the low metal ion valence and the geometrical conditions. It must be emphasized, however, that adduct molecules may very well be formed by weak bonds as long as the geometrical conditions are more favourable, that is in the presence of tetrahedral coordination. Thus the ammonium ion forms an adduct of this type in $NH_4X \cdot 3NH_3$ (1960: 2) in which the discrete molecule (Fig. 1) is held together by hydrogen bonds.

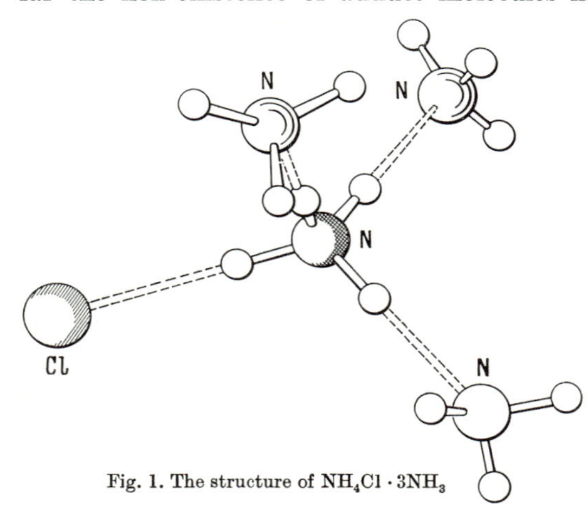


Fig. 1. The structure of $NH_4Cl \cdot 3NH_3$

**Beryllium.** The beryllium halides react in a very regular way, generally forming adducts $BeX_2 \cdot 2D$ or $BeX_2 \cdot 4D$. It is probable that the former type is always a monomeric molecule with tetrahedral coordination around the beryllium atom. It has been assumed that the latter type is a salt $(BeD_4)Cl_2$, and it has therefore been excluded from the systematic treatment. Conclusive experimental evidence for these assumptions is still lacking, but it seems highly improbable that beryllium exceeds tetrahedral coordination in compounds of this type.

**Magnesium.** All the magnesium halides including $MgI_2$ exhibit octahedral coordination around the magnesium atom. There is, therefore, no reason to assume that a lower coordination occurs in their adducts unless the experimental evidence is very convincing, but no proof has been given for tetrahedral coordination in the adducts with different donor molecules. Compounds of the type $(MgD_6)X_2$ are formed as a rule but adducts with four donor molecules, a case which would correspond to possible molecule formation, do not occur. Compounds $MgX_2 \cdot 2D$ are again more common and in the literature these compounds have generally been assumed to be molecular adducts with tetrahedral coordination. However, they could quite easily have octahedral coordination with halogen bridges between the magnesium atoms. Although the question of their structures must be left open until conclusive experimental evidence has been obtained, they have been included in the systematic treatment. For the same reason not all the compounds $MgX_2 \cdot D$ have been omitted, since they might exist as bridged tetrahedral molecules.

**Other alkaline earth metals.** The comments on the alkali metals are also applicable here, except that only four donor molecules are necessary for molecule formation. On the other hand it is well known that strontium and barium can have a higher coordination than six and in this event the probability of adduct molecule formation is even less.

**Zinc.** The stereochemistry of zinc is complicated by the confirmed existence of two types of coordination, tetrahedral and octahedral, both of which are quite common. The coordination in the hydroxide is octahedral, and the salt hydrates generally contain $Zn(H_2O)_6^{2+}$ ions. Octahedral coordination has also been found in the zinc salt of glycyl-glycine (1962: 1).

On the other hand the diammoniates $ZnBr_2 \cdot 2NH_3$ and $ZnCl_2 \cdot 2NH_3$ exhibit tetrahedral coordination and are molecular adducts (1936: 1). Tetrahedral coordination is also reported for the zinc salts of imidazol and mercaptoethanolamine (1962: 2, 3), and $ZnCl_2$ forms an adduct molecule with thiosemicarbazide which has tetrahedral coordination (1960: 3) (Fig. 2). Zinc also has tetrahedral coordination in all the modifications of $ZnCl_2$ (1959: 60). Finally the $ZnCl_4^{2-}$ ion is tetrahedral in $Na_2ZnCl_4 \cdot 3H_2O$ (1960: 4).

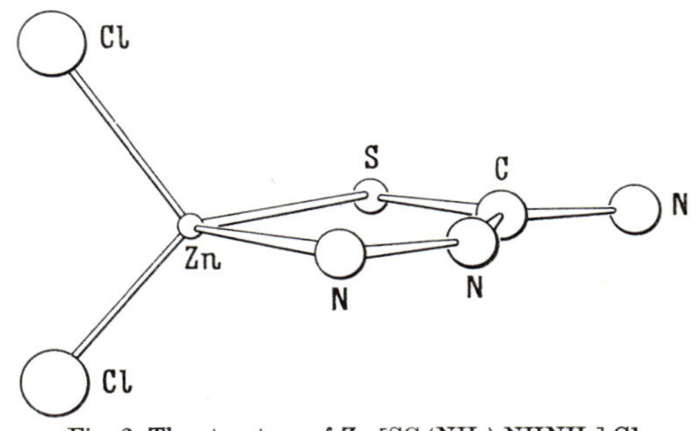

Fig. 2. The structure of Zn [SC $(NH_2)$ $NHNH_2$] $Cl_2$

In any discussion of the zinc coordination, it might be of value to note the suggestion made by ORGEL (1960: 5) that oxygen as a ligand favours octahedral coordination, while nitrogen and sulfur lead to tetrahedral arrangements. However, it has been suggested on good evidence that tetrahedral coordination may exist in $Zn[(C_6H_5)_3PO]_4(ClO_4)_2$ (1960: 6).

**Cadmium.** Cadmium shows the same dualism of coordination as zinc. The six-fold coordination is, however, more pronounced for cadmium, as is demonstrated by the difference between the crystal structures of the diammoniates. In contrast to the tetrahedral coordination and molecular structure of $ZnX_2 \cdot 2NH_3$ there is octahedral coordination with infinite halogen bridges in $CdX_2 \cdot 2NH_3$ (1936: 2). Similar structures are also found for *bis*-biuret-cadmium chloride (1960: 7) (Fig. 3) and *bis*-urea-cadmium chloride (1957: 1). On the other hand tetrahedral coordination is highly probable in adducts with phosphines and arsines, although the coordination is far from regular (1940: 1). Compounds $CdX_2 \cdot 2D$ are therefore included in the systematic section although in most cases they probably contain infinite halogen bridges.

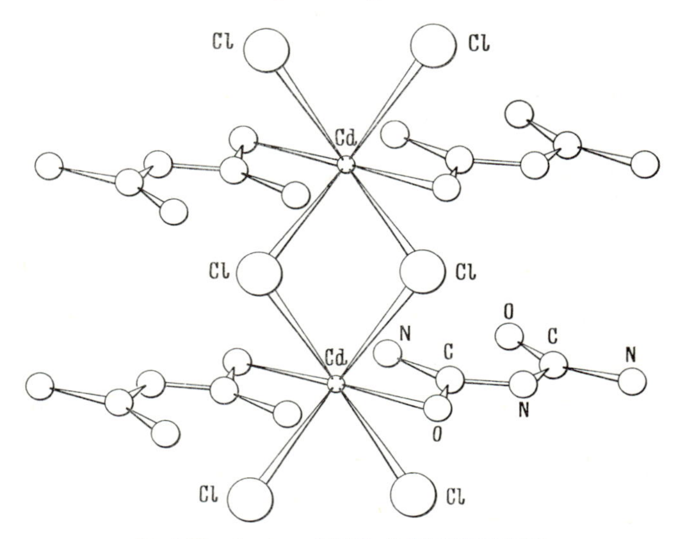


Fig. 3. The structure of $CdCl_2 \cdot 2\,NH_2CONHCONH_2$

**Mercury.** In the light of the known crystal structures it seems reasonable to assume that there are two main types of mercury halide adducts. In the first type, weak adduct formation with oxygen and nitrogen seems to have little influence on the shape of the $HgCl_2$ molecule, and the donors interact at rather large distances. This conclusion is based on the following structure determinations: $HgCl_2 \cdot C_4H_8O_2$ (dioxane) (1954: 1), $HgCl_2 \cdot C_6H_{14}O_4$ (naphthodioxane) (1956: 1), $HgCl_2 \cdot C_9H_6O_2$ (coumarin) (1953: 1) and $HgCl_2 \cdot 2C_5H_5N$ (1956: 2). (The structure of $HgCl_2 \cdot 2NH_3$ (1936: 2) is quite different, however.) In all these compounds the coordination around the mercury atom can be described as distorted octahedral, with two short bonds to the halogen atoms and longer bonds to the oxygen or nitrogen atoms. The full, distorted octahedral coordination is achieved by the formation of still longer bonds to an appropriate number of halogen atoms in the neighbouring $HgX_2$ molecules so that the correct composition is obtained. The distortion appears to decrease on passing from $HgCl_2$ to $HgI_2$ adducts. (Cf. the structures of $HgCl_2$ and $HgI_2$.) Variations of the mole ratio, $HgX_2$: donor molecule, are easily explained by this assumption, but discrete adduct molecules are not always formed.

In the second type of mercury halide adduct, strong adduct formation with oxo-compounds and with phosphines and arsines leads to a distorted type of tetrahedral coordination, and the different mole ratios are explained by different degrees of halogen bridge formation *and* by weak interaction between excess $HgX_2$ molecules and polymeric adduct molecules. The experimental evidence for this is provided by the molecular adduct $HgCl_2 \cdot 2(C_6H_5)_3PO$ (and the corresponding arsine oxide adduct) (1962: 4) (Fig. 10) and by adducts with phosphines and arsines (1940: 1). Finally it should be noted that with thioethers, substitution reactions have been reported, and molecular adducts are not obtained although the composition would indicate it (1962: 5).

It remains for crystal structure studies to show how many of the $HgX_2$ adducts included in the systematic treatment are actually adduct molecules. The number is probably small, but this class of compound certainly presents a very intriguing problem for structural chemistry.

**Boron.** Boron has a very great tendency to form molecular addition compounds, and there is a large amount of relevant literature. The following crystal structures are known: $BF_3 \cdot NH_3$ (1951: 1), $BF_3 \cdot CH_3NH_2$ (1950: 1; 1951: 3), $BF_3 \cdot (CH_3)_3N$ (1951: 2, 3), $BF_3 \cdot C_5H_5N$ (1956: 3), $BF_3 \cdot CH_3CN$ (1950: 2) and $BF_3 \cdot (CH_3)_2SO$ (1962: 6). In all cases the coordination around the boron atom is tetrahedral. It is noteworthy that the tetrahedral arrangement is never quite regular, and regular trends in the distortions may occur. Further studies are necessary before a detailed discussion of this problem is possible. In cases where internal exchange occurs, as in $BH_3 \cdot NH_3$ ($= BH_2(NH_3)_2^+ + BH_4^-$) the tetrahedral coordination is also prevalent, and no other possibility need be considered.

**Aluminium.** No crystal structure determinations have been reported for molecular adducts with aluminium halides. Evidence makes it fairly probable that the coordination is tetrahedral in the common 1:1 adducts, and it has been assumed in the following treatment that 1:1 adducts are molecules. There are, however, uncertain cases, since it is well known that aluminium also exhibits octahedral coordination in many simple binary compounds and in a number of hydrates. As a rule 1:2 adducts and in some cases even 1:3 adducts have been included in the systematic section, in the absence of further structure studies.

**Scandium, yttrium and rare earth metals.** The discussion of the alkaline earth metals can be directly applied to these elements, in which there is the same possibility for high coordination and the same small probability of molecular adduct formation. In some cases, however, it seems quite possible that the six-fold coordination is preserved and that adduct molecules are actually obtained. One example is provided by $La(NO_3)_3 \cdot 3(C_4H_9O)_3PO$ (1959: 1). Such adducts have not been included in the systematic section, however, since structural evidence is lacking and also because they are so well covered in all the recent treatises on lanthanide and actinide extraction. Nevertheless it would be a mistake to neglect these compounds altogether and their existence should be remembered in this connection.

**Gallium, indium and thallium.** No structure determinations of adducts with the halides of these elements have been reported. It seems quite probable that the 1:1 adducts have tetrahedral coordination, but the occurrence of 1:2 and 1:3 adducts with ethers and amines indicate the possibility of higher coordinations.

**Silicon, germanium, tin and lead, titanium, zirconium and hafnium.** The characteristic coordination for all these elements in adducts of the tetravalent halides seems to be the octahedral one, even if in the instance of the 1:1 adducts the experimental evidence is not quite complete. The structures of the following compounds are known: $GeCl_4 \cdot 2C_5H_5N$ (1960: 8), $SnCl_4 \cdot 2SeOCl_2$ (1960: 9) (Fig. 16), $SnCl_4 \cdot 2POCl_3$ (Fig. 8) and $TiCl_4 \cdot 2POCl_3$ (1962: 7) and $SnCl_4 \cdot 2(CH_3)_2SO$ (1962: 8) (Fig. 14). The 1:1 adduct $TiCl_4 \cdot POCl_3$ is dimeric and also exhibits octahedral coordination (1960: 1) (Fig. 9). With polydentate ligands, coordination numbers higher than six might be possible, particularly in the compounds of zirconium and hafnium.

**Phosphorus.** The typical coordination for pentavalent phosphorus is tetrahedral. Octahedral coordination does not seem to be very favourable and pentavalent phosphorus compounds have very weak acceptor properties. The pentachloride can acquire chloride ions to form the octahedral $PCl_6^-$ ion, but the oxide chloride $POCl_3$ does not exhibit any tendency to add donor molecules or ions (1958: 3). (Convincing evidence has been presented for the adduct $POCl_3 \cdot HCON(CH_3)_2$ being a salt-like compound (1959: 2).) The trivalent phosphorus compounds are also poor acceptor molecules.

**Arsenic, antimony, bismuth, niobium, tantalum.** All the 1:1 adducts of the pentavalent compounds of these elements have been assumed to be molecular adducts with octahedral coordination. The structures of the following compounds are known: $SbCl_5 \cdot POCl_3$ (1959: 3) (Fig. 7), $SbCl_5 \cdot (CH_3)_3PO$ (1961: 2) (Fig. 7), $SbCl_5 \cdot (C_6H_5)_2SO$ (1962: 9) (Fig. 13), $SbCl_5 \cdot (CH_3)_2SO_2$ (1962: 10) (Fig. 15), $SbCl_5 \cdot HCON(CH_3)_2$ (1962: 11), $SbCl_5 \cdot SeOCl_2$ (1962: 12) (Fig. 17), $NbCl_5 \cdot POCl_3$ and $TaCl_5 \cdot POCl_3$ (1962: 13) (Fig. 7).

The trivalent halides of arsenic, antimony and bismuth form 1:1 and 1:2 adduct molecules whose structures are unknown, with the exception of $SbCl_3 \cdot 2(C_6H_5)_3AsO$ (1962: 14). In this structure the five ligands form a distorted tetragonal pyramid around the antimony atom with the two oxygen atoms in *cis* positions (Fig. 11).

**Sulfur, selenium, tellurium, chromium, molybdenum, tungsten.** Very few adducts have been prepared containing these elements as acceptor atoms and, in general, their characteristic coordination numbers can only be guessed. The structure of $SeOCl_2 \cdot 2C_5H_5N$, in which $SeOCl_2$ is the acceptor molecule, exhibits a selenium coordination which is very similar to that of antimony in the $SbCl_3$ 1:2 adduct mentioned above. In the selenium compound, however, the pyridine molecules are in the *trans* position (1959: 4) (Fig. 4).

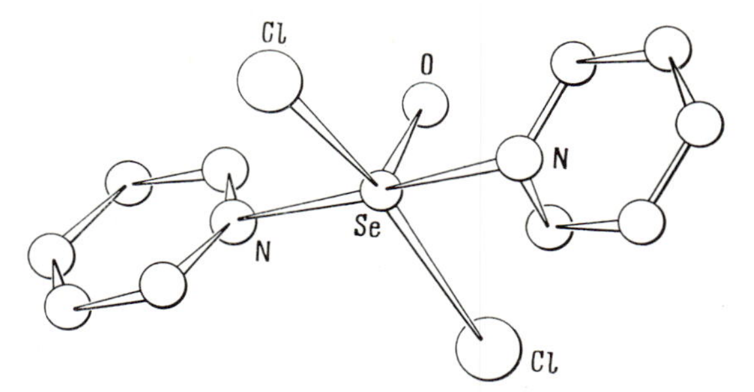


Fig. 4. The structure of $SeOCl_2 \cdot 2C_5H_5N$

**Actinides.** For the lower valencies of this group the discussion relating to the rare earth metals can be applied. For the higher valencies the analogy lies more closely with the corresponding main group of metallic elements and the possibility of adduct molecule formation is accordingly greater. Examples of such compounds are $Np(NO_3)_4 \cdot 2(C_4H_9O)_3PO$ (1959: 1) and $UO_2(NO_3)_2 \cdot 2(C_2H_5O)_3PO$ (1960: 10). In respect of these compounds, however, the list of references given in the systematic section is incomplete. (See comment on rare earth metals).

**Transition elements.** As was mentioned earlier, metal halides which do not form discrete molecules can still form molecular adducts, and typical examples are to be found among the halides of the transition elements. In this instance the main problem is to decide whether octahedral, tetrahedral or a square coplanar configuration results. In any case, if the chemical compositions are to be used as a basis for predicting the existence of molecular adducts, it is necessary to know whether the coordination number is four or six. Thus compounds with the composition $CoCl_2 \cdot 2D$ could be either molecular adducts with tetrahedral coordination or bridged structures with octahedral coordination. Both types are encountered among the transition elements and only a few examples need be given to indicate the difficulties in making safe predictions.

The most conclusive evidence is that obtained from crystal structure determinations, and the results of two such determinations are mentioned here. The adduct $CoCl_2 \cdot 2p—CH_3C_6H_4NH_2$ (1957: 2) is molecular with tetrahedral coordination, but in one modification of $CoCl_2 \cdot 2C_5H_5N$, the coordination is octahedral and the structure contains chlorine bridges (1957: 3). The availability of more than one coordination number seems to be the rule for the elements manganese, iron, cobalt and nickel, and the reader is referred to the original literature and to a recent book by ORGEL (1960: 5) for more detailed studies.

Some attemps have been made recently to obtain details of coordination from UV and visible spectra and measurements of magnetic moments. Predictions in respect of both spectra and magnetic moments derived from the ligand field theory and empirical comparisons seem to permit a distinction between different types of coordination (different orbital contributions). Many of the conclusions based on such studies argue convincingly in support of tetrahedral coordination in cobalt (II) compounds (1960: 6, 11, 12, 13; 1962: 16), square coplanar coordination in copper (II) compounds (1960: 6, 11), tetrahedral coordination in some nickel (II) compounds (1960: 12, 14, 15) and planar coordination in others (1960: 11) and tetrahedral coordination in manganese (II) compounds (1961: 3; 1962: 16).

More surprising are the seemingly well-founded suggestions regarding the tetrahedral coordination in copper (II) compounds (with phosphine oxides but not with arsine oxides) (1961: 4) and the planar coordination in some manganese adducts (1960: 6; 1961: 3). If these unexpected configurations can be confirmed by means of complete structure determinations, the success of the predictions will constitute a triumph for the ligand field theory.

Most of the adducts mentioned above contain phosphine or arsine oxides acting as donor molecules. Evidence has been obtained which indicates that the sulfoxides behave similarly in a number of adducts. Compounds in which there are three donor molecules for each acceptor atom are of special interest. All the evidence (magnetic moment, spectra, metathetic reactions) points towards an internal exchange of halide ions and sulfoxide molecules resulting in the formation of ionic compounds such as $[Co((CH_3)_2SO)_6]CoX_4(=CoX_2 \cdot 3(CH_3)_2SO)$ (1960: 16, 17; 1961: 5, 6). Adducts of this composition have been included in the systematic section for purposes of comparison.

It is probable, however, that the adducts with the transition elements are incompletely covered, and in this connection it should be explained that initially it was intended to exclude them from this treatment.

It can be assumed that $FeCl_3$ forms adducts $FeCl_3 \cdot D$ with tetrahedral coordination, but no definite evidence of this has been presented. Octahedral coordination is also possible and the adducts $FeCl_3 \cdot 2D$ might have bridged structures.

**Iodine and bromine.** Iodine and similar molecules have been shown to give adducts with different donor molecules. The interaction is generally weak and its character is slightly different from that of the cases under discussion, owing to the different types of acceptor atom involved. They are therefore excluded from the systematic treatment but the reader is referred to the original literature for details of these very interesting compounds, which have been extensively studied by HASSEL and his students (1962: 29). In this connection the structure of $Br_2 \cdot (CH_3)_2CO$ might be of interest to the reader (1959: 61).

A review is found in a monograph by G. BRIEGLEB: Elektronen – Donator – Acceptor – Komplexe, Springer-Verlag, 1961.

## 4. Structural evidence concerning donor molecules

The formation of adducts by donor-acceptor reactions has very different effects on the acceptor and donor molecules, a fact which becomes evident when the conditions for molecular adduct formation are considered. The changes of coordination in the acceptor molecules are often so complex as to necessitate detailed structural studies, while the donor molecules experience little structural change on combination. In some cases, however, it is not immediately evident which atom is the donor, or whether an alternative ion transfer has taken place. Before beginning the systematic treatment it is useful to see how far the available structural evidence can settle such problems, and which questions remain open for discussion.

It is indisputable that X-ray crystallography offers the most conclusive evidence on these points, but the structural studies in this field are unfortunately very few. On the other hand spectroscopic methods have been used extensively in this connection and in most cases very convincing results have been obtained. It is unnecessary to quote the results of some spectroscopic studies which are clearly obsolete; such failures have occurred frequently in the application of molecular spectroscopy to all fields of chemistry.

The principle behind the spectroscopic studies is that adduct formation at an oxygen atom will always lead to a decrease in the strength of the bond between the oxygen atom and the rest of the donor molecule. In the infrared or Raman spectra a change of this kind should be associated with a decrease in the frequency of the vibrational mode assumed to be characteristic of the bond which is weakened. Changes in adjacent bonds have also been considered to some extent. It has been pointed out that purely kinematic effects would lead to an increase in the frequency, so that the actual decrease due to bond weakening is, in fact, larger than that measured by the direct frequency shift (1960: 18, 19; 1961: 7).

The possibility of coupling with other vibrations has been given little attention. The spectroscopic method can be employed in an empirical, diagnostic approach and its use in this respect will be demonstrated below. There are doubtful cases in which caution must be observed, as is shown by the fact that adduct formation at the nitrogen in nitrile leads to an *increase* in the CN vibration frequency (1958: 4, 5; 1960: 20).

In oxo-compounds, oxygen is bound to one other atom. The only atoms which need be considered are carbon, nitrogen, phosphorus, arsenic, sulfur and selenium, and the possible donors will be treated in this order.

**Donor molecules containing the group $>C=O$.** In the simplest case, namely that of *aldehydes, ketones* and *quinones*, it is generally obvious that the addition is made to the oxygen atom. No structure determinations have been made but a large number of spectroscopic studies indicate a weakening of the $C=O$ bond. The examples comprise all types of acceptor molecules: $ZnX_2$ (1958: 6; 1960: 21; 1961: 8), $HgX_2$ (1957: 4; 1959: 5,

6; 1961: 8), $BF_3$ (1957: 5; 1958: 6, 7; 1961: 8), $AlX_3$ (1954: 2, 3; 1958: 4, 6), $Al(OR)_3$ (1960: 22), $SnCl_4$ (1958: 4), $TiCl_4$ (1958: 8; 1960: 18), $AsCl_3$ and $SbCl_3$ (1960: 23), $SbCl_5$ (1961: 8), $MoOCl_3$ (1962: 21) and $FeCl_3$ (1958: 6). Accordingly it seems that a decrease in the C=O vibration frequency is a fairly safe indication of adduct formation at the oxygen atom and that this can be used diagnostically to study less obvious cases.

The first problem is offered by *esters, carboxylic acids, acid anhydrides* and *lactones*, all of which contain one ether oxygen bonded to the carbon atom of the C=O bond. One structure determination has been made, namely that of

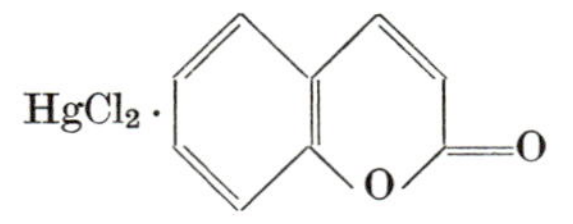


(coumarin) (1953: 1). This shows clearly that the C=O bond oxygen is the donor atom. It was long held that in pyrones the bridge oxygen atom possessed the donor properties (1915: 1). Spectroscopic studies have demonstrated a weakening of the C=O bond in adducts with esters (1958: 9; 1960: 24; 1961: 7, 9, 55; 1962: 19), carboxylic acids (1961: 9), acid anhydrides (1954: 2), lactones (1959: 5) and $\gamma$-pyrones (1961: 8). In all these cases a strengthening of the adjacent C—O bond has also been observed. All possible donor molecules belonging to these types have been included in the systematic treatment.

A suggestion that both oxygen atoms are donors in 2:1 adducts of $TiCl_4$ with diesters (1961: 55) is not very convincing.

*Amides* and *urea* (and related compounds) present the next problem. Here the structural evidence is ample, thanks to the systematic studies by NARDELLI and CAVALCA. The adducts which have been studied are not molecular but they clearly show that oxygen is the donor atom. Compounds of this type are $CdCl_2 \cdot 2NH_2CONHCONH_2$ (1960: 7), $CdCl_2 \cdot CH_3CONH_2$ (1957: 6), $CdCl_2 \cdot 2(NH_2)_2CO$ (1957: 1) and $CdCl_2 \cdot NH_2CONHCH_3$ (1958: 10). The same result was found in a recent study of $SbCl_5 \cdot HCON(CH_3)_2$ (1962: 11). Spectroscopic evidence points in the same direction, and in this connection adducts with the following acceptor molecules have been studied: $MgCl_2$ (1960: 25), $BF_3$ (1959: 7), $BCl_3$ and $BBr_3$ (1960: 26), $SnCl_4$ (1961: 10) and $TiX_4$ (1958: 11; 1960: 27). The controversial suggestions originally made for $SiF_4 \cdot 2HCON(CH_3)_2$ (1954: 4) and $CdCl_2 \cdot CH_3CONHCH_3$ (1959: 8) have since been rejected or queried (1960: 26, 28). A final striking exception is $SnBr_4 \cdot 2(NH_2)_2CO$ (1961: 10), which should not form an adduct at the oxygen atom, in contrast to the corresponding $SnCl_4$ adduct.

In a study of complex formation between urea and metal halides it was found that most metal ions form complexes with the oxygen atom (Cr(III), Fe(III), Zn(II) and Cu(II)) but some also form with the nitrogen atom (Pd(II) and Pt(II)) (1957: 7).

Amide and urea adducts have generally been included in the systematic treatment.

There are a great number of problems of this type which cannot be discussed in detail here. A few examples should be mentioned, however. If the same molecule contains both ether and acyl oxygen atoms which are not bound to the same carbon atom, the question of the donor function is quite open and such adducts have been included in the systematic treatment as far as possible.

Many adducts have been reported with pyrimidone

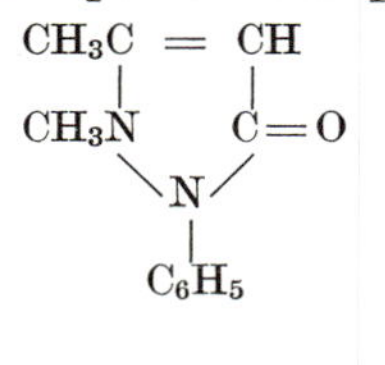

and antipyrine

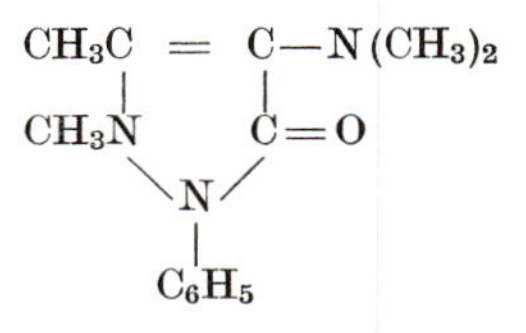

(1915: 2; 1923: 1; 1930: 1; 1944: 1; 1947: 1) which might contain some donor-acceptor bonds to the oxygen atom, but this field has not been covered in the systematic treatment.

Results obtained in the studies of *acyl halides* as donor molecules are more conflicting. Unfortunately crystal structure determinations are lacking. Spectroscopic studies indicate bonding to oxygen in the following cases: $AlX_3 \cdot C_6H_5COCl$ (1954: 2; 1958: 12), $AlCl_3 \cdot C_{17}H_{35}COCl$ (1960: 22), $TiCl_4 \cdot C_6H_5COCl$ (1960: 29) and $TiCl_4 \cdot o{-}CH_3C_6H_4COCl$ (1961: 11). The reports regarding $AlCl_3 \cdot CH_3COCl$ are very confusing. Initially an increase of the C=O frequency was reported (1957: 8); following this, both decrease and increase were found (1959: 9) and the impossible suggestion was made that both types of bonding are present in the solid adduct i. e. $CH_3CO^+AlCl_4^-$ and $Cl_3AlOC\langle{}^{Cl}_{CH_3}$ coexist. Later the same conflicting views were expressed in connection with $TiCl_4 \cdot CH_3COCl$ (1959: 10; 1960: 29; 1961: 12). However, a reasonable explanation has since been given for these divergent results. Thus it was found that the increased frequencies appeared after an interval, suggesting that they might originate in irreversible side reactions which are easily catalyzed by Lewis acids (see p. 83). It seems fair to say that at present there is more convincing evidence for bonding to oxygen than for halide ion transfer, although it is quite possible that both cases actually occur. Until further studies have been made it is only possible to quote the additional evidence for halide ion transfer. Thus adducts of both types are reported between very similary substituted benzoyle chlorides and $AlCl_3$ and $TiCl_4$. It is less surprising that $BF_3 \cdot CH_3COF$ differs from these and in this instance the ionic nature of the compound seems to be very well established (1957: 9). It would be very interesting to study $SbCl_5 \cdot CH_3COCl$ by spectroscopic methods, since conductivity measurements in $SO_2$ indicate its complete dissociation into $CH_3CO^+$ and $SbCl_6^-$ (1944: 2).

All acyl halide adducts have been included in the systematic treatment, but they have been treated separately as a special class.

**Donor molecules containing the group $>$NO.** Negative shifts of the NO vibration frequency have been reported for adducts with pyridine oxide (1961: 13; 1962: 21).

**Donor molecules containing the group —$NO_2$.** Only one class of compound will be discussed, namely the organic *nitro compounds*. (Adducts with $NO_2F$ are almost certainly ionic compounds (1960: 30).) The question in respect of structure is whether both or only one of the oxygen atoms functions as donors (1958: 13). No structure determinations have been made and some spectroscopic studies constitute the only evidence. Two papers deal with adducts between $AlCl_3$ or $TiCl_4$ and $C_6H_5NO_2$ and report different results, but with the same conclusion that only one of the oxygen atoms functions as a donor (1957: 10; 1958: 14). The adducts $SbCl_5 \cdot C_6H_5NO_2$ (1957: 10), $AlCl_3 \cdot CH_3NO_2$ (1961: 14) and $AlBr_3 \cdot CH_3NO_2$ (1958: 14) have also been studied. It has been suggested (1958: 14; 1961: 14) that the simultaneous increase of the antisymmetric and decrease of the symmetric —$NO_2$ vibration frequencies support the view that nitro compounds are only monofunctional donor molecules. In addition the negative shift of the symmetrical vibration frequency is roughly in parallel with the positive shift of a lower frequency which, in a series of adducts between para-substituted nitrobenzenes and $AlBr_3$, has been interpreted as an Al—O stretching frequency.

**Donor molecules containing the group —N=O.** Nitroso and nitrosyl compounds belong to this type of molecule. In the organic nitroso compounds the oxygen atom is probably the donor but no experimental proof of this has been offered. With the nitrosyl halides, ion transfer associated with the formation of complex nitrosyl salts is also possible. The structure determination of $BF_3 \cdot NOF$ (1937: 1) and the Raman spectroscopic studies of $AlCl_3 \cdot NOCl$ (1953: 2; 1958: 4) all indicate the occurrence of ion transfer. In the case of the spectroscopic studies, this conclusion is based on the increase of the NO vibration frequency. The adducts with nitrosyl halides have therefore not been included in the systematic treatment, but it is possible that there are adducts other than those studied structurally which have different configurations. A further search for such adducts should be based on Asmussen's division of the nitrosyl halide adducts into three different types (1939: 1) and on the results of the preliminary exchange experiments (1956: 4; 1957: 11).

**Donor molecules containing the group $>$P=O.** The typical representatives of this type of donor molecule are *phosphine oxides* $R_3PO$, *esters* of *phosphoric acid* $(RO)_3PO$ and *phosphoryl halides* $POX_3$. All kinds of mixed derivatives formed between these three types are also possible but their behaviour as donor molecules has not been studied very extensively. Structure determinations show that oxygen is the donor atom not only in adducts with phosphine oxides such as $SbCl_5 \cdot (CH_3)_3PO$ (1961: 2) but also in adducts with phosphoryl halides such as $SbCl_5 \cdot POCl_3$ (1959: 3), $NbCl_5 \cdot POCl_3$ and $TaCl_5 \cdot POCl_3$ (1962: 13), $SnCl_4 \cdot 2POCl_3$ and $TiCl_4 \cdot 2POCl_3$ (1962: 7) and $(TiCl_4 \cdot POCl_3)_2$ (1960: 1).

The negative shift of the P=O vibration frequency in adducts with phosphine oxides has been extensively verified, (1958: 12; 1959: 11; 1960: 11, 14, 19, 23; 1961: 3, 4; 1962: 15, 21) and has also been used to demonstrate that addition to the oxygen atom occurs in adducts with esters of phosphoric acid (1960: 31) and with phosphoryl halides (1958: 12; 1959: 10, 12, 13; 1960: 23, 32). Exceptions are reported for adducts of $BCl_3$ with $(C_6H_5O)_2POCl$ and $C_6H_5OPOCl_2$ (1960: 31). The compound $BCl_3 \cdot POCl_3$ constitutes a difficult case. Initially a positive shift of 12 $cm^{-1}$ was reported (1960: 31), then a negative shift of 100 $cm^{-1}$ was claimed (1960: 33) and later discounted (1961: 15). An important feature of the latter paper is the assignment of $BCl_3$ and $BCl_4^-$ "envelopes". The latest contribution (1962: 15) states definitely that the compound exhibits a negative frequency shift of 130 $cm^{-1}$ and that the $BCl_4^-$ assignment has no value since similar frequencies are found in $BBr_3 \cdot POBr_3$. This frequency shift should instead be attributed to the B—O donor-acceptor bond. Although the arguments put forward in this last paper seem most convincing, and the alternative process of halogen transfer requires much stronger evidence than has been obtained, the problem obviously cannot be considered as settled. All adducts with donor molecules of this type have been included in the systematic treatment.

**Donor molecules containing the group $\gt$As=O.** Only arsine oxide adducts have been studied, but it is interesting to note that both negative shifts (1961: 4, 16; 1962: 21) and positive shifts (1961: 3) of the As=O vibration have been observed, although it is evident that donor-acceptor bonds with the oxygen atoms must exist in all the compounds.

**Donor molecules containing the group $\gt$S=O.** The typical representatives are *sulfoxides*, $R_2SO$, *esters* of *sulfurous acid* $(RO)_2SO$ and *thionyl halides* $SOX_2$. All kinds of mixed derivatives are also possible. The occurrence of addition to the oxygen atom has been established by the crystal structure determinations of $SbCl_5 \cdot (C_6H_5)_2SO$ (1962: 9), $SnCl_4 \cdot 2(CH_3)_2SO$ (1962: 8) and $BF_3 \cdot (CH_3)_2SO$ (1962: 6).

Negative shifts of the S=O vibration frequency have also been reported (1960: 16, 17, 34; 1961: 5, 28) except for adducts with $PdCl_2$ and $PtCl_2$, for which it has been assumed that sulfur is the donor atom (1960: 16, 34; 1961: 28). A negative shift has also been found in $AlCl_3 \cdot SOCl_2$ (1958: 12), indicating that the oxygen atom is the donor atom in thionyl halides, too. All adducts of this type have been included in the systematic treatment.

**Donor molecules containing the group $\gt S \lt^{O}_{O}$.** The typical representatives are *sulfones* $R_2SO_2$, *esters* of *sulfuric acid* $(RO)_2SO_2$ and *sulfuryl halides* $SO_2X_2$. All kinds of mixed derivatives are also possible. The crystal structure of the compound $SbCl_5 \cdot (CH_3)_2SO_2$ (1962: 10) (Fig. 15) shows that in this instance only *one* of the oxygen atoms is used as a donor but this need not be true of all such adducts. All adducts of this type are included in the systematic treatment.

**Donor molecules containing the group >Se = O.** The typical representatives are *selenium oxides* $R_2SeO$, *esters* of *selenious acid* $(RO)_2SeO$ and *selenium oxide halides* $SeOX_2$. All kinds of mixed derivatives are also possible. The crystal structure determinations of $SbCl_5 \cdot SeOCl_2$ (1962: 12) (Fig. 17) and $SnCl_4 \cdot 2SeOCl_2$ (1960: 9) (Fig. 16) show that the oxygen atom is the donor in these adducts. Similar conclusions have been reached as a result of spectroscopic studies, which indicate a weakening of the Se = O bond (1958: 12; 1959: 10). It has been suggested that in $HgCl_2 \cdot R_2SeO$ the selenium atom is the donor (1951: 4). Although probably correct, clear evidence for this view is lacking and a structure determination is needed. In most cases, however, it can be assumed that the oxygen atom is the donor, and all adducts of this type are included in the systematic treatment.

**Elements which do not form oxo-compounds.** The preceding treatment of donor-acceptor adducts has been of a rather formal character; discussion of the chemical bonds involved is deferred to later chapters. However, the reader who is familiar with the periodic system may wonder why no molecules containing the groups —B = O and > Si = O have been included. The answer is that such compounds do not seem to exist. Compounds having compositions which suggest the presence of such groups are in fact polymeric; two single bonds are formed with oxygen instead of one double bond. The corresponding reaction also occurs occasionally with compounds containing C = O bonds, as is shown by the polymerization of aldehydes, but the tendency to polymerization is much more pronounced in boron and silicon chemistry. It might be expected that such compounds would be depolymerized through strong interaction with Lewis acids, so that adducts would be obtained despite the non-existence of the free donor molecules. No such adducts appear to be described, however, but no very determined efforts to prepare them are evident. Information is also very sparse regarding compounds containing > Ge = O and > Sn = O bonds, but some interesting compounds have recently been reported (1949: 1; 1951: 5).

## 5. Adducts with donor molecules containing the group >C=O

This group of compounds comprises by far the largest number of adduct molecules studied. A number of cases in which the donor function is uncertain have already been discussed in the preceding chapter, and only a few comments will be added at this stage. In most cases of aliphatic amino substitution it can safely be assumed that the amino nitrogen is the most important donor atom; consequently only doubtful instances have been included in the systematic treatment. In the case of the aromatic amino ketones (1925: 1) and amino esters (1952: 2) the situation is less certain owing to the well-known fact that the amino groups donate electrons to the aromatic ring, but no further references will be given.

Similarly, in instances where it can safely be assumed that some other atom is the donor the compounds have been excluded. Typical examples are adducts between donors containing both oxygen (as part of a C=O bond) and sulfur, and acceptor molecules such as $HgCl_2$ and $PdCl_2$, which are known to have a strong affinity for sulfur as a donor atom.

In the following section, the different types of donor molecules containing C=O bonds will be treated in the same order as in the preceding chapter for each type of acceptor *atom*. Comments will be made on individual compounds only if their classification as adduct molecules is not obvious, or if some other information of interest can be added.

The phrase "and similar adducts" is used to indicate that other adducts with the same type of donor, the same acceptor atom and the same mole ratio have been described. Thus, as a rule, the different halides of a given acceptor atom are not presented separately, nor, for instance, are the adducts of different types of ketones. Exceptions to this rule are made whenever an isolated compound is of special interest.

**Lithium**

$LiBr \cdot 2(CH_3)_2CO$ (1930: 2)
$LiBr \cdot (CH_3)_2C{=}CHCOCH_3$ and similar adducts (1952: 1)
$LiI \cdot 2(NH_2)_2CO$ and similar adducts (1956: 5; 1958: 15, 16)
$LiI \cdot (NH_2)_2CO$ (1958: 17)

The chief reason for including these adducts is to show that the organic donor molecules containing C=O bonds can also form addition compounds with the alkali and alkaline earth metal halides (corresponding calcium and strontium adducts have also been described), although it is almost certain that they are not molecular adducts.

**Beryllium**

$BeCl_2 \cdot 2C_6H_5CHO$ (1925: 3; 1928: 1)
$BeCl_2 \cdot 2(CH_3)_2CO$ (1925: 4; 1928: 1)

Some remarkable ternary adducts of these compounds with benzene have also been reported (1925: 4)

$BeCl_2 \cdot 2C_6H_5CONH_2$ (1959: 14)

**Magnesium**

$MgBr_2 \cdot 3C_6H_5CHO$ (1907: 1)
$MgBr_2 \cdot 2C_6H_5CHO$ and similar adducts (1904: 1; 1925: 5)
$MgCl_2 \cdot$ (furan ring, O)—CHO (1939: 2)
$MgBr(C_2H_5) \cdot C_6H_5CH{=}CHCHO$ and similar adducts with Grignard reagents (1924: 1; 1925: 5)
$MgBr_2 \cdot 3(CH_3)_2CO$ and similar adducts (1907: 1; 1927: 1)

$MgCl_2 \cdot 2(CH_3)_2CO$ and similar adducts (1904: 1; 1927: 1; 1939: 2, 3; 1955: 1; 1956: 6)

$MgI(CH_3) \cdot C_6H_5COCH_3$ and similar adducts with Grignard reagents (1902: 1; 1939: 4, 1949: 2; 1956: 6)

The importance of adduct formation in Grignard reactions, with particular reference to the mechanism of the reduction of ketones, has been discussed in a number of papers; in some the opinions expressed are highly controversial (1921: 1; 1924: 1; 1925: 5; 1939: 4; 1951: 6; 1952: 2).

$MgBr(C_2H_5) \cdot C_6H_5COC_6H_4NH_2$ and similar adducts (1939: 4)

When magnesium is the acceptor atom, there is no obvious reason why nitrogen should be preferred as a donor, and these adducts of aromatic amino ketones probably contain Mg—O bonds. It is, however, very doubtful if they are molecular adducts.

$MgCl_2 \cdot 3CH_3COOC_2H_5$ and similar adducts (1909: 1, 2; 1937: 2)
$MgBr_2 \cdot 2C_6H_5COOR$ and similar adducts (1909: 1; 1907: 2; 1939: 2)
$MgCl_2 \cdot CH_3COOC_2H_5$ (1937: 2)
$MgBr_2 \cdot 2CH_2(COOC_2H_5)_2$ and similar adducts (1909: 1; 1904: 1)

Mixed adducts with aldehydes or esters and Grignard reagents or $MgBr_2$ have also been prepared (1905: 1).

$MgCl_2 \cdot 4CH_3COOH$ (1934: 1; 1937: 2)
$MgCl_2 \cdot 4HCON(CH_3)_2$ and similar adducts (1956: 7; 1958: 17; 1960: 25)
Similar adducts with amino esters and ureas (1909: 2)
$MgCl_2 \cdot 3HCON(CH_3)_2$ (1961: 17)
$MgBr_2 \cdot 2CH_3CONH_2$ (1909: 1)

**Calcium**

$CaBr_2 \cdot 2(CH_3)_2CO$ (1930: 2)
$CaCl_2 \cdot 2HCOOC_2H_5$ (1909: 1)
$CaCl_2 \cdot CH_3COOCH_3$ (1909: 3)

The last paper is quoted since, apart from the description of adduct formation with $CaCl_2$, it also demonstrates how a large number of inorganic reactions can occur in methylacetate as a solvent.

**Zinc**

$ZnI_2 \cdot 2(CH_3)_2CO$ and similar adducts (1910: 1; 1924: 2)
$2ZnBr_2 \cdot 3(CH_3)_2CO$ (1924: 2)

Both these compounds have remarkably low melting points, $+ 45$–$47^0$ and $+ 32$–$34^0$ respectively, indicating molecular structures. If the 2 : 3 adduct is a dimeric molecule it must be unsymmetrical. A structure determination would be of great interest.

$ZnCl_2 \cdot (C_6H_5)_2CO$ and similar adducts (1912: 1; 1958: 6)
$2ZnBr_2 \cdot (CH_3)_2CO$ (1930: 2)

$ZnCl_2 \cdot$ [phenanthrenequinone: =O, =O] (1908: 1)

$ZnCl_2 \cdot$ [2,6-dimethyl-γ-pyrone: $H_3C$, O, $CH_3$, C, O]

and similar $\gamma$-pyrone adducts (1910: 1; 1961: 8)
$ZnCl_2 \cdot (C_6H_5)_2C=NN(C_6H_5)(COCH_3)$ (1950: 3)
In this hydrazone adduct oxygen is probably the donor atom.
$ZnCl_2 \cdot CH_3COOC_{10}H_{17}$(i) (1930: 3)
$ZnCl_2 \cdot CH_3C(=NC_6H_5)CH_2COOC_2H_5$ (1950: 4)

Some other adducts of substituted anils of $\beta$-ketoesters have been reported. The anils of simple aldehydes and ketones do not give such adducts; this indicates that the oxygen of the $C=O$ bond is the donor atom. It has been suggested that $ZnCl_2$ could be used analytically to distinguish anils of $\beta$-ketoesters from the anils of simple aldehydes and ketones.

$2ZnCl_2 \cdot 3CH_3COOH$ (1946: 1)
$ZnCl_2 \cdot (CH_3CO)_2O$ (1959: 15)
$3ZnCl_2 \cdot 2(CH_3CO)_2O$ (1959: 15)
$ZnSO_4 \cdot 4RCONH_2$ (1960: 35)
$ZnCl_2 \cdot 2(NH_2)_2CO$ (1857: 1; 1957: 7, 12)
$ZnCl_2 \cdot CH_3CONHC_2H_4NHCOCH_3$ and similar adducts (1926: 1; 1947: 2)
$ZnCl_2 \cdot C_6H_5N(COCH_3)_2$ (1952: 3)
$2ZnCl_2 \cdot 3HCONHC_6H_4CH=CHCOC_6H_5$ (1926: 1)

**Cadmium**

$CdCl_2 \cdot$ [furfural: O, CHO] and similar adducts (1949: 3; 1959: 5)
$2CdCl_2 \cdot C_6H_5CHO$ (1949: 3)
Anil adducts as with $ZnCl_2$ (1950: 4)
$2CdCl_2 \cdot 3CH_3COOH$ (1945: 1)
$CdCl_2 \cdot CH_3COOH$ and similar adducts (1945: 1, 2)
$2Cd(CH_3COO)_2 \cdot CH_3COOH$ (1945: 2)
$CdCl_2 \cdot (CH_3CO)_2O$ (1959: 15)

$CdCl_2 \cdot$ [coumarin: O, =O] (1959: 5)

$Cd(NO_3)_2 \cdot 4(NH_2)_2CO$ (1958: 16)

$CdCl_2 \cdot 2HCONH_2$ and similar adducts (1886: 1; 1958: 18; 1960: 35)

$CdCl_2 \cdot 2(NH_2)_2CO$ (two modifications) (1957: 12; 1958: 19)

$CdCl_2 \cdot C_6H_5CONH_2$ and similar adducts (1923: 2)

$CdCl_2 \cdot (NH_2)_2CO$ and similar adducts (1857: 1; 1957: 12; 1958: 19)

$CdCl_2 \cdot 2NH_2CONHCONH_2$ (1904: 2)

It is interesting to observe that this compound is not a molecular adduct with octahedral coordination as might have been expected. Only one of the oxygen atoms functions as a donor atom. A complete structure determination has been carried out (1960: 7) (Fig. 3).

$CdCl_2 \cdot OC\langle^{CH_2NH}_{NHCH_2}\rangle CO$ (1929: 1)

**Mercury**

$HgCl_2 \cdot C_6H_5CHO$ and similar adducts (1902: 2; 1904: 3; 1945: 3; 1959: 5)

$2HgCl_2 \cdot C_6H_4(OH)CHO$ (1945: 3)

$HgCl_2 \cdot (C_6H_5)_2CO$ and similar adducts (1892: 1; 1903: 1; 1904: 3, 4; 1906: 1; 1910: 1; 1915: 1; 1923: 3; 1945: 3; 1959: 5)

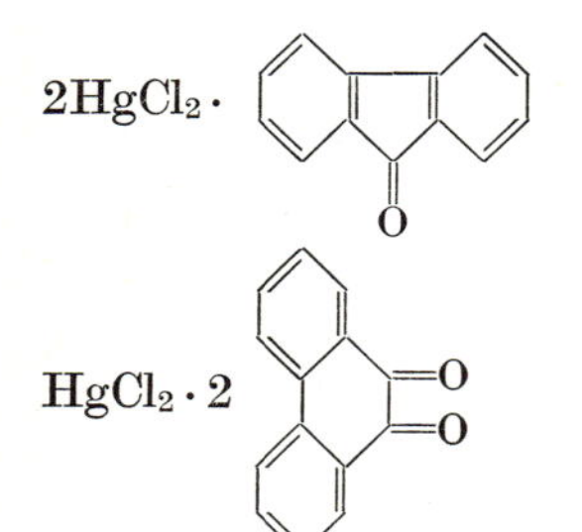


(1910: 2)

(1908: 1)

$HgCl_2 \cdot CH_3COCH_2COCH_3$ (1945: 3)

Anil adducts as with $ZnCl_2$ (1950: 4)

$HgCl_2 \cdot 2CH_3COOH$ (1938: 1)

$HgCl_2 \cdot$ [2,6-dimethyl-4-pyrone: $H_3C$, $CH_3$, O, O] (1908: 2; 1953: 1; 1959: 5)

$HgCl_2 \cdot$ [coumarin: O, =O] (1961: 8)

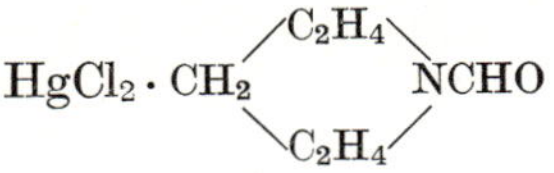

$HgCl_2 \cdot CH_2 \begin{matrix} C_2H_4 \\ \\ C_2H_4 \end{matrix} NCHO$ and similar adducts (1886: 1; 1954: 5)

$HgCl_2 \cdot (NH_2)_2CO$ (1896: 1; 1957: 12)

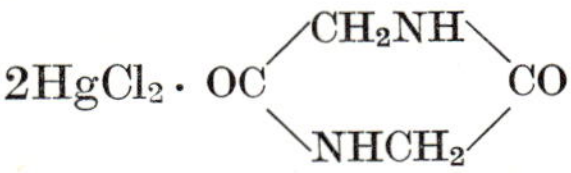

$2HgCl_2 \cdot OC \begin{matrix} CH_2NH \\ \\ NHCH_2 \end{matrix} CO$ (1929: 1)

$2HgCl_2 \cdot (CH_3)_3N^+CH_2COO^-$ (1938: 2)

A number of adducts with betains have been reported in this paper. The mole ratio varies from 6:1 to 2:1. Similar salt adducts are described with LiCl, $CaCl_2$ and some other halides (1915: 2). The oxygen coordination is known with certainty (cf. the structure of a glycine adduct with $FeSO_4 \cdot 5H_2O$ (1960: 36)) but the detailed coordination is very uncertain, as in most $HgCl_2$ adducts.

$HgCl_2 \cdot (C_6H_5)_3Sb = NCOCH_3$ (1954: 6)

This is a peculiar compound which should be studied further.

**Boron**

$BF_3 \cdot CH_3CHO$ and similar adducts (1879: 1; 1939: 5; 1957: 13)

The reactions between $BCl_3$ and aldehydes generally lead to atomic rearrangements but at least one 1:1 and one 2:3 adduct have been described (1957: 14).

$BF_3 \cdot (CH_3)_2CO$ and similar adducts (1879: 1; 1894: 1; 1939: 5; 1957: 13; 1958: 6, 7)

The reactions between $BCl_3$ or $BBr_3$ and ketones generally lead to organo-boron compounds (1944: 3; 1948: 1).

$BF_3 \cdot C_6H_5COCH_2COCH_3$ (1934: 2)

$B_2Cl_4 \cdot 2(CH_3)_2CO$ (1961: 18)

This is an exceptional type of adduct.

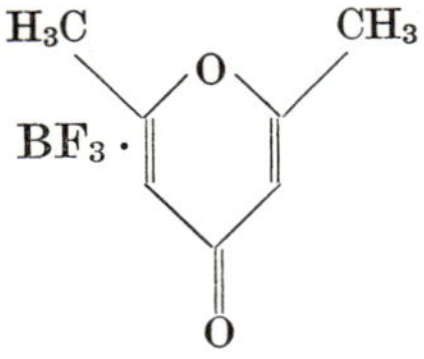

$BF_3 \cdot$ (2,6-dimethyl-4-pyrone: ring O with $H_3C$ and $CH_3$ substituents, C=O at position 4) (1961: 8)

$BF_3 \cdot HCOOCH_3$ and similar adducts (1931: 1; 1932: 1; 1952: 4; 1953: 3; 1961: 7)

$BCl_3 \cdot CH_3COOC_2H_5$ (1955: 2; 1956: 8; 1961: 7)

This and similar $BCl_3$ adducts decompose easily.

$BF_3 \cdot HCOOH$ and similar adducts (1927: 2; 1931: 1; 1934: 3)

$BF_3 \cdot (COOH)_2$ and similar adducts (1934: 3)

$BF_3 \cdot [(CH_3CO)_2CHCO]_2O$ (1934: 3)

This and a similar adduct are formed when $BF_3$ and $(CH_3CO)_2O$ react with the elimination of water (see p. 82) between the original anhydride molecules under the influence of the $BF_3$ molecule. The donor function is not clear.

$BF_3 \cdot$ (cyclic: $CH_2$—CO—O—CO—$CH_2$, ring with $CH_2$—$CH_2$ bond) (1932: 2)

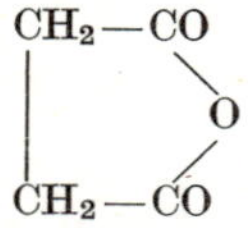

$3BF_3 \cdot (CH_3CO)_2CHCOOCOCH(COCH_3)_2$ (1934: 2)

Similar complicated keto-anhydride adducts have been prepared, and they have been shown to be monomolecular in acetic acid (1934: 2).

$BF_3 \cdot$ (cyclic: $CH_2$—$CH_2$—CO—O—$CH_2$, ring closed by $CH_2$—$CH_2$) and similar adducts (1955: 3)

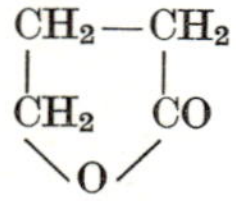

$BF_3 \cdot HCON(CH_3)_2$ and similar adducts (1931: 1; 1932: 3; 1953: 4; 1959: 7)

$BCl_3 \cdot CH_3CONH_2$ and similar adducts (1960: 37)

$BF_3 \cdot (NH_2)_2CO$ (1956: 9)

**Aluminium**

$AlCl_3 \cdot C_6H_5CHO \cdot CH_3OH$ (1917: 1)

The structure of this ternary compound (and a similar ketone adduct) is very uncertain; it has been included since it is the only aldehyde adduct which could be found in the literature, in contrast to the large number of ketone adducts.

$AlCl_3 \cdot (C_6H_5)_2CO$ and similar adducts (1893: 1; 1896: 3; 1900: 1; 1901: 1; 1902: 3; 1910: 2, 3; 1912: 2; 1928: 2, 3; 1932: 4; 1951: 7; 1958: 6)

Exceptional 1:2 (1912: 2) and 3:5 (1929: 2) adducts have been reported without clear evidence.

$2AlBr_3 \cdot C_6H(CH_3)_3(COCH_3)_2$ (1928: 2)

$3AlBr_3 \cdot C_6H_3(COCH_3)_3$ (1928: 2)

$2AlCl_3 \cdot C_6H_4$ (—CO— / —CO— bridged) $C_6H_4$ and similar adducts (1902: 3; 1953: 5)

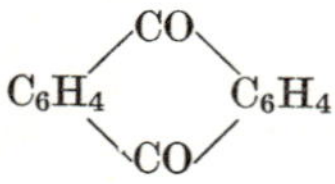

These examples indicate that the di- and triketones may use all their oxygen atoms as donor atoms.

$AlBr_3 \cdot CH_3COCH_2COCH_3$ and similar adducts (1902: 3)

$AlCl_3 \cdot$ [phenanthrenequinone structure: two benzene rings with C=O, C=O] (1908: 1)

These examples on the other hand show that not all the donor functions are always used.

$2AlBr_3 \cdot CH_3COC_6H_4OCH_3$ (1928: 2)

$3AlBr_3 \cdot (CH_3OC_6H_4)(CH_3OC_6H_4CH=CH)CO$ (1928: 2)

These compositions indicate that ether oxygen atoms might also be used for adduct formation. Some independent physico-chemical evidence is desirable, however. In the last case the simple 1:1 adduct also exists, and in this probably only the C=O oxygen functions as a donor atom, but no 1:2 adduct has been found.

$AlCl_3 \cdot C_6H_5COC_6H_4NO_2$ (1900: 1)

Both *meta* and *para* isomers have been prepared. In this case it can quite definitely be assumed that the C=O oxygen is the donor atom (Cf. the relative donor strengths p. 60).

$AlCl_3 \cdot C_6H_4(CO)_2C_6H_3NH_2$ (1953: 5)

2:1 and 3:1 adducts are also reported, and it is probable that first both oxygen atoms and then the nitrogen atom are used as donor atoms.

$AlCl_3 \cdot CH_3COOCH_3$ and similar adducts (1880: 1; 1893: 1; 1904: 5; 1910: 4; 1940: 2; 1961: 7)

$AlCl_3 \cdot (COOC_2H_5)_2$ (1904: 5)

All the diesters studied have given 1:1 adducts.

With aliphatic acids HCl is generally evolved and aluminium salts are formed. Some adducts have been isolated, however, and some of them have a very puzzling composition.

$4AlCl_3 \cdot CH_3COOH$ (1904: 2)

Also similar adducts with esters (1904: 2; 1917: 1)

It has been shown by infrared studies, without isolation of actual compounds, that $AlCl_3$ and $AlBr_3$ form adducts with acid anhydrides (1954:2). In addition, the 1:1 adducts with phenolphthalein, its dimethylether and its chinoid methylester are of great interest (1907: 1; 1911: 1).

$AlCl_3 \cdot$ (HOOC)(H)C=C(H)(COOH) (1917: 1)

$AlCl_3 \cdot CH_3CONHC_6H_4CH_3$ (1894: 2)

$AlCl_3 \cdot NH_2COOC_2H_5$ (1896: 2)

**Gallium**

$GaCl_3 \cdot (CH_3)_2CO$ (1958: 20; 1960: 38)
$Ga(CH_3)_3 \cdot (CH_3)_2CO$ (1953: 6)
$GaCl_3 \cdot CH_3COOC_2H_5$ (1961: 7)

**Indium**

$InCl_3 \cdot CH_3COOC_2H_5$ and similar adducts (1961: 7; 1962: 25)

**Silicon**

($SiCl_4 \cdot 2CH_3COCH_2COOC_2H_5$ (1955: 4))
The non-existence of this adduct has since been claimed in a paper (1959: 16) which contains many valuable observations regarding the difficulties of studying $SiCl_4$ adducts.
$SiF_4 \cdot 2HCON(CH_3)_2$ (1954: 4; 1960: 28)
However, no adducts are formed with
$CH_3COOC_2H_5$ (1961: 7)

**Germanium**

$GeF_4 \cdot 2HCON(CH_3)_2$ (1960: 28)

**Tin**

$SnCl_4 \cdot 2C_6H_5CHO$ and similar adducts (1904: 6; 1910: 5; 1911: 1; 1922: 1; 1927: 3; 1936: 3; 1960: 39)
$SnCl_4 \cdot 2(C_6H_5)_2CO$ and similar adducts (1910: 1, 2, 5; 1911: 1; 1916: 1; 1922: 1; 1924: 3; 1925: 6; 1936: 3; 1962: 26)
$SnBr_4 \cdot (C_6H_5CH=CH)_2CO$ (1904: 6)
This is an exceptional 1:1 adduct with a ketone.
$SnCl_4 \cdot C_6H_5COCOC_6H_5$ and similar adducts (1908: 1; 1925: 7)
$SnCl_4 \cdot C_6H_5COCH=CHCOC_6H_5$ (*cis* and *trans*) (1924: 4)

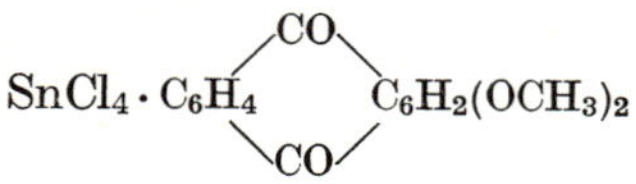

$SnCl_4 \cdot C_6H_4\langle{}^{CO}_{CO}\rangle C_6H_2(OCH_3)_2$ (1913: 1)

Here the oxygen atoms of the C=O bonds are probably used as donor atoms.
Both 1:1 and 1:2 adducts with indigo derivatives have also been prepared (1930: 4).
$SnCl_4 \cdot 2C_6H_5COCOC_6H_5$ (1908: 1)

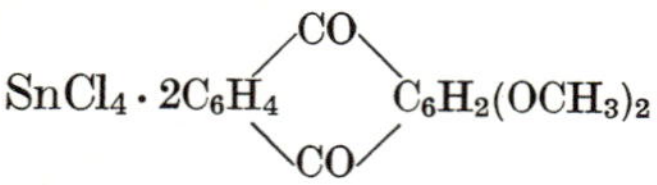

$SnCl_4 \cdot 2C_6H_4\langle{}^{CO}_{CO}\rangle C_6H_2(OCH_3)_2$ (1913: 1)

In these compounds the diketones are only monofunctional donors where the adducts have molecular structures.
$SnCl_4 \cdot O=C_6H_4=O$ and similar adducts (1908: 1; 1960: 39)

With rather large diketones and quinones 1:2 adducts have also been reported (1926: 2) but the conditions are complicated by the fact that the corresponding unsaturated hydrocarbons also add $SnCl_4$ molecules in many cases (1936: 4).

$SnCl_4 \cdot 2(CH_3)_2NC_6H_4CHO$ (1911: 1)
$SnCl_4 \cdot (CH_3)_2NC_6H_4CH{=}CHCOC_6H_5$
and similar adducts (1925: 1)

The composition of the latter compound indicates that both nitrogen and oxygen might be donor atoms. In the preceding compound the question is quite open.

$SnCl_4 \cdot 2C_6H_5COOC_2H_5$ and similar adducts (1904: 6; 1910: 5; 1914: 1; 1924: 5; 1938: 3; 1944, 4; 1956: 10; 1959: 17; 1961: 7, 9)

$SnCl_4 \cdot 2$ ($CH_2O$—CO—$OCH_2$, cyclic: $CH_2O$ / $CH_2O$ joined to CO) (1961: 19)

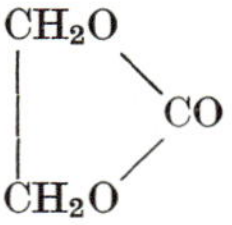

$SnBr_4 \cdot (C_2H_5O)_2CO$ (1914: 1)
$SnCl_4$ on the other hand gives a 1:2 adduct.
$SnCl_4 \cdot C_6H_5COOC_2H_5$ (1923: 4; 1924: 5)

This is the only 1:1 adduct of $SnCl_4$ which has been reported.
$SnCl_3(CH_3) \cdot C_6H_5CH{=}CHCOOC_2H_5$ (1914: 1)
$SnCl_4 \cdot 2NH_2C_6H_4COOC_2H_5$ and similar adducts (1925: 8)

It is suggested in this paper that the nitrogen atom is the donor atom.

$SnCl_4 \cdot (COOC_2H_5)_2$ and similar adducts (1914: 1, 2; 1924: 4; 1938: 3, 4; 1961: 55)

It should be noted that esters of both fumaric and maleic acid give 1:1 adducts (1924: 4).
The introduction of still more ester groups does not result in an altogether regular increase in the mole ratio $SnCl_4$: donor but the trend is obvious:

$3SnCl_4 \cdot 2C_3H_5(COOC_2H_5)_3$ (1925: 2)
$3SnCl_4 \cdot C_2H_2(COOC_2H_5)_4$ (1925: 2)
$4SnCl_4 \cdot C_2H_2(COOC_2H_5)_4$ (1925: 2)

$SnCl_4 \cdot CH_3COOC_6H_4CHO$ (1911: 1)
$SnCl_4 \cdot CH_3COCH_2COOC_2H_5$ (1903: 2; 1955: 4)
This $\beta$-kotoester is thus a bifunctional donor.
$SnCl_4 \cdot 2C_6H_5COOH$ and similar adducts (1904: 6; 1910: 5; 1914: 1; 1947: 3)
$SnCl_4 \cdot 2NH_2CH_2COOH$ (1956: 11)

$SnCl_4 \cdot 2(CH_3CO)_2O$ is referred to in (1932: 2)

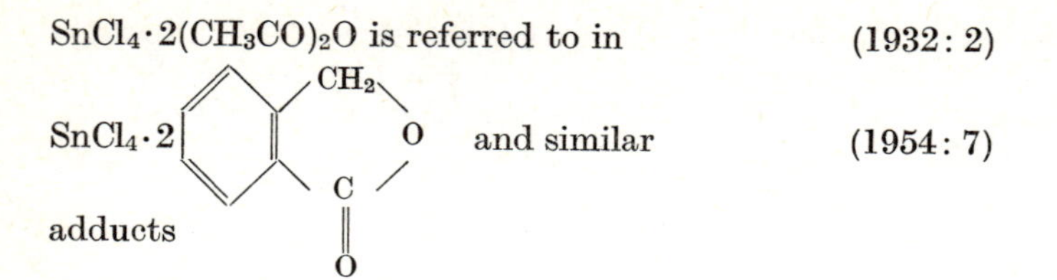

(1954: 7)

Both 1:1 and 1:2 adducts have been reported with substituted phenolphthaleins (1907: 3; 1940: 3)

$SnF_4 \cdot 2HCON(CH_3)_2$ (1960: 28)
$SnCl_4 \cdot 2C_6H_5CONH_2$ and similar adducts (1910: 5; 1911: 1)
$SnCl_4 \cdot C_6H_5N(COCH_3)_2$ (1952: 3)
$SnF_4 \cdot 2[(CH_3)_2N]_2CO$ (1960: 28)
$SnCl_4 \cdot 2(NH_2)_2CO$ and similar adducts (1958: 21; 1961: 10)

**Titanium**

$TiF_4 \cdot CH_3CHO$ and similar adducts (1958: 22)
$TiCl_4 \cdot 2$ (O-ring)—CHO and similar adducts (1927: 4; 1960: 39)
$TiF_4 \cdot 2(CH_3)_2CO$ (1960: 28)
$TiF_4 \cdot (C_2H_5)_2CO$ (1958: 22)
$TiCl_4 \cdot 2(C_6H_5)_2CO$ (1932: 5)
$TiCl_4 \cdot (C_6H_5)_2CO$ and similar adducts (1927: 4; 1932: 5; 1933: 1; 1952: 5)
$TiCl_4 \cdot CH_3COCH_2COCH_3$ (1903: 2)
$TiCl_4 \cdot O{=}C_6H_4{=}O$ (1960: 39)
$TiCl_4 \cdot 2CH_3COOC_2H_5$ and similar adducts (1873: 1; 1961: 19; 1962: 25)
$TiCl_4 \cdot CH_3COOC_2H_5$ and similar adducts (1873: 1; 1952: 6; 1956: 10, 12, 13; 1958: 23; 1961: 7; 1962: 19, 25)
$2TiCl_4 \cdot CH_3COOC_2H_5$ (1873: 1; 1958: 23)
The latter adduct is very unstable (1958: 23)
$TiCl_4 \cdot 2(C_2H_5OOC)CH{=}CH(COOC_2H_5)$ (1932: 5)
$TiCl_4 \cdot (COOC_2H_5)_2$ and similar adducts (1873: 1; 1927: 4; 1932: 5; 1958: 9, 22; 1961: 55)
$2TiCl_4 \cdot (COOC_2H_5)_2$ and similar adducts (1873: 1; 1932: 5; 1961: 55)
$TiCl_3(OC_2H_5) \cdot CH_3COOC_2H_5$ and similar adducts (1952: 6)
$TiCl_4 \cdot CH_3COCH_2COOC_2H_5$ (1955: 4)
$TiCl_4$ adducts with acetylated sugars have also been prepared (1960: 40).
$TiCl_4 \cdot C_6H_5N{=}NC_6H_4OCOC_6H_5$ (1934: 4)
$TiF_4 \cdot 2CH_3COOH$ (1960: 28)
$TiF_4 \cdot 2HCON(CH_3)_2$ (1960: 28)
$2TiCl_4 \cdot 5HCON(CH_3)_2$ (1960: 41)

$TiCl_4 \cdot 2CH_3CON(C_6H_5)_2$ and similar adducts (1934: 4; 1958: 11; 1960: 27, 28, 41)
$TiCl_4 \cdot CH_3CONHCH_3$ (1960: 37)
$TiCl_3(HCONH) \cdot 2HCONH_2$ (1958: 11)

$$TiCl_4 \cdot \begin{array}{ccc} & C_2H_4 & \\ OC & & CO \\ & NH & \end{array}$$ (1934: 4)

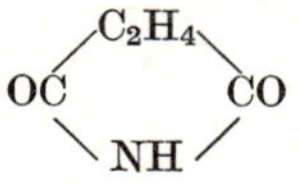

$TiF_4 \cdot [N(CH_3)_2]_2CO$ (1960: 28)

**Zirconium**

$ZrCl_4 \cdot 2(C_6H_5)_2CO$ and similar adducts (1927: 5)
$ZrCl_4 \cdot (CH_3)_2CO$ (1959: 18)
$ZrCl_4 \cdot 2C_6H_5COOC_2H_5$ and similar adducts (1907: 4; 1952: 7, 8, 9; 1959: 19; 1962: 25)
$ZrCl_4 \cdot CH_3COOC_3H_7$ and similar adducts (1907: 4; 1927: 5; 1950: 5; 1959: 19, 20)
$ZrCl_3(OC_2H_5) \cdot CH_3COOC_2H_5$ and similar adducts (1950: 5)
$ZrCl_2(OC_2H_5)_2 \cdot CH_3COOC_2H_5$ (1950: 5)
$ZrCl_4 \cdot C_6H_4(COOC_2H_5)_2$ and similar adducts (1954: 8; 1961: 55)
$ZrF_4 \cdot HCON(CH_3)_2$ (1960: 28)
$ZrF_4 \cdot [N(CH_3)_2]_2CO$ (1960: 28)

**Hafnium**

$HfCl_4 \cdot 2C_6H_5COOCH_3$ (1952: 8, 9)
$HfCl_4 \cdot C_6H_4(COOC_2H_5)_2$ (1954: 8)

**Thorium**

$ThCl_4 \cdot 2CH_3CHO$ and similar adducts (1903: 3; 1919: 1)
$ThCl_4 \cdot 2(CH_3)_2CO$ and similar adducts (1903: 3; 1919: 1)

However, there are also some adducts with mole ratios which might indicate a higher coordination than octahedral for thorium:

$ThCl_4 \cdot 4C_6H_5COCH_3$ and similar adducts (1904: 6; 1919: 1; 1934: 5)
$2ThBr_4 \cdot 7C_6H_5COCH_3$ (1934: 5)
$ThBr_2(C_6H_5COO)_2 \cdot 3C_6H_5CHO$ (1934: 5)
$ThBr_4 \cdot 2CH_3COOC_2H_5$ (1934: 5)
$ThCl_4 \cdot C_6H_4(OH)COOCH_3$ (1919: 1)
but also:
$ThBr_4 \cdot 3C_6H_5COOC_2H_5$ (1934: 5)

**Phosphorus**

$PCl_3 \cdot 3C_6H_5CHO$ (1955: 5)
It is very doubtful if this is an adduct molecule.

**Arsenic**

$AsCl_3 \cdot (CH_3)_2CO$ (1960: 23)

**Antimony**

| | |
|---|---|
| $SbCl_5 \cdot CHO$ and similar adducts | (1901: 2; 1904: 6; 1959: 21) |
| $SbCl_3 \cdot C_6H_5CHO$ and similar adducts | (1913: 2) |
| $SbCl_5 \cdot (CH_3)_2CO$ and similar adducts | (1901: 2; 1959: 21) |
| $2SbCl_5 \cdot (C_6H_5)_2CO$ | (1908: 1) |
| $SbCl_5 \cdot$ ($H_3C$, $CH_3$, O, O) | (1961: 8) |
| $SbCl_3 \cdot 2(CH_3)_2CO$ | (1960: 23) |
| $SbCl_3 \cdot C_6H_5COCH_3$ and similar adducts | (1912: 3; 1924: 5) |
| $SbCl_5 \cdot CH_3COCH_2COCH_3$ and similar adducts | (1903: 2) |
| $SbCl_5 \cdot O=C_6H_4=O$ | (1960: 39) |

The preceding two donors seem to be only monofunctional, in contradistinction to:

| | |
|---|---|
| $2SbCl_5 \cdot$ (O, O) and similar adducts | (1908: 1; 1960: 39) |

For adducts with complicated quinones see comment under tin.

| | |
|---|---|
| $SbCl_5 \cdot CH_3COOC_2H_5$ and similar adducts | (1901: 2; 1902: 4; 1959: 22; 1961: 9) |
| $SbCl_5 \cdot (C_2H_5O)_2CO$ and similar adducts | (1902: 4; 1959: 22) |
| $SbCl_3 \cdot CH_3COOC_{10}H_{17}$(i) | (1930: 3) |
| $2SbCl_5 \cdot 3C_6H_5CH=CHCOOC_2H_5$ | (1904: 6) |
| $2SbCl_5 \cdot (COOC_2H_5)_2$ and similar adducts | (1902: 4; 1924: 4) |
| $3SbCl_5 \cdot CH_2(COOC_2H_5)CH(COOC_2H_5)CH_2COOC_2H_5$ | (1902: 4) |
| $2SbCl_5 \cdot CH_3COCH_2COOC_2H_5$ | (1902: 4) |
| $SbCl_5 \cdot CH_3COOH$ and similar adducts | (1902: 4; 1959: 22; 1961: 9) |
| $2SbCl_5 \cdot 3C_6H_5CH=CHCOOH$ | (1904: 6) |
| $SbCl_3 \cdot CH_3COOH$ and similar adducts | (1912: 3; 1951: 8, 9) |
| $2SbCl_5 \cdot (COOH)_2$ and similar adducts | (1901: 2; 1902: 4) |
| $2SbCl_5 \cdot 3$ (O, C, O, C, O) | (1901: 2) |

$2SbCl_5 \cdot 5(CH_3CO)_2O$ (1959: 15)
$SbCl_3 \cdot (CH_3CO)_2O$ (1959: 15)
With substituted phenolphthaleins 1:1 adducts are formed (1940: 3)
$SbCl_5 \cdot HCON(CH_3)_2$ (1962: 11)
$2SbCl_5 \cdot 3CH_3CONH_2$ (1901: 2)
$SbCl_3 \cdot C_6H_5CONHC_6H_5$ and similar adducts (1925: 9)
$2SbCl_3 \cdot C_6H_5CONHC_6H_5$ and similar adducts (1925: 9)
It should be observed that the above list contains a number of surprising mole ratios, and the 2:3 adducts in particular seem to be worth a more thorough study.

**Bismuth**

$2BiCl_3 \cdot (CH_3CO)_2O$ (1959: 15)

**Vanadium**

$VOCl_3 \cdot 2C_6H_5CHO$ (1954: 9)
$VCl_4 \cdot 2C_2H_5CHO$ and similar adducts (1954: 9)
$VCl_3 \cdot 2CH_3COOC_2H_5$ (1959: 23)

**Tantalum**

$TaCl_5 \cdot (CH_3)_2CO$ and similar adducts (1923: 5)

**Sulfur**

$SOCl_2$ adducts with ketones have not been isolated but their existence in solution has been quite clearly established (1955: 6)
$SO_2 \cdot (CH_3)_2CO$ (1945: 4)
The constitution of this and similar adducts of $SO_2$ (1910: 2) is most uncertain.
Atomic rearrangements may very well have occurred.
$SO_3$ forms 3:2 and 2:1 adducts with polycyclic ketones (1948: 2)

**Molybdenum**

$MoF_4 \cdot 2HCON(CH_3)_2$ (1960: 28)

**Uranium**

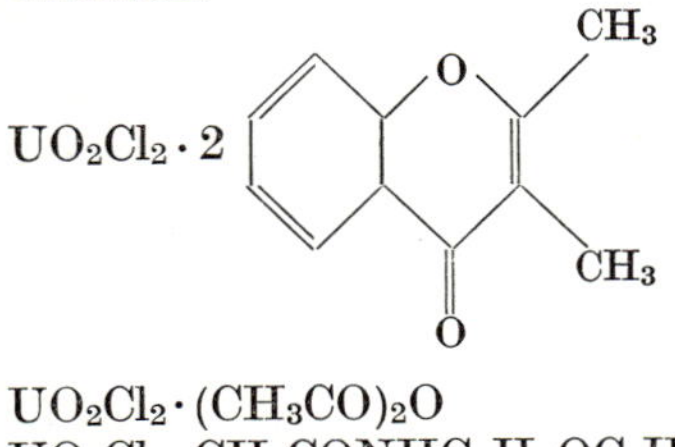

(1915: 1)

$UO_2Cl_2 \cdot (CH_3CO)_2O$ (1938: 5)
$UO_2Cl_2 \cdot CH_3CONHC_6H_4OC_2H_5$ (1931: 2)

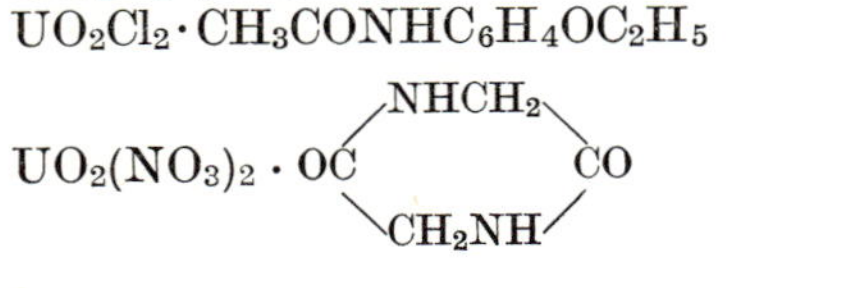

(1929: 1)

$UO_2(CH_3COO)_2 \cdot 4CO(NH_2)_2$ (1961: 20)
$UO_2(CH_3COO)_2 \cdot 2CO(NH_2)_2$ (1961: 20)
$UO_2(CH_3COO)_2 \cdot CO(NH_2)_2$ (1961: 20)

**Manganese**

$MnI_2 \cdot 2CH_3COOC_2H_5$ (1958: 24)
$MnBr_2 \cdot CH_3COOC_2H_5$ (1958: 24)
$MnCl_2 \cdot 4RCONH_2$ (1960: 35)
A mixed adduct is reported on p. 38

**Rhenium**

$ReCl_2 \cdot 4CH_3COOH$ (1958: 25)
$ReCl_2 \cdot CH_3COOH$ (1958: 25)

**Iron**

$FeCl_3 \cdot (C_6H_5)_2CO$ and similar adducts (1903: 4; 1904: 6, 7)
$2FeCl_3 \cdot (C_6H_5CH=C_2H_2=CH)_2CO$ and similar adducts (1904: 6)

$FeCl_3 \cdot 2$ (2,3-dimethylchromone; $CH_3$, O, $CH_3$, O) (1915: 1)

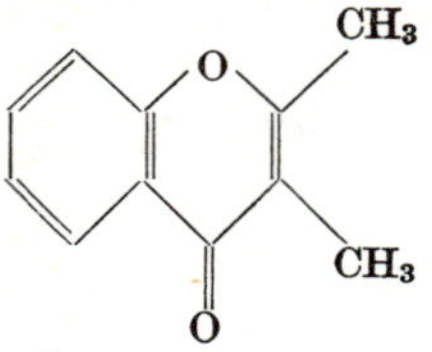

$FeCl_3 \cdot 3$ (=O, =O) (1908: 1)

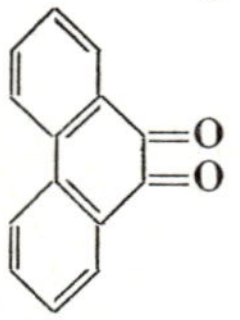

$FeCl_3 \cdot 2CH_3COOC_2H_5$ (1961: 7)
$FeCl_3 \cdot C_6H_5CH=CHCOOC_2H_5$ (1904: 6)
$FeCl_3 \cdot C_6H_5CH=CHCOOH$ (1904: 6)
$2FeCl_3 \cdot 3(CH_3CO)_2O$ (1959: 15)

**Cobalt**

$CoCl_2 \cdot 2(CH_3)_2CO$ (1956: 14)
$CoCl_2 \cdot (CH_3)_2CO$ and similar adducts (1930: 2)
$CoCl_2 \cdot 4RCONH_2$ (1960: 35)
$CoCl_2 \cdot RCONH_2$ (1886: 1)
$CoCl_2 \cdot (NH_2)_2CO$ (1959: 24)

**Nickel**

$NiCl_2 \cdot 4RCONH_2$ (1960: 35)
$NiCl_2 \cdot RCONH_2$ (1886: 1)
$NiCl_2 \cdot NH_2CONHNH_2$ (1936: 5)

The suggested coordination with oxygen and the terminal nitrogen of the hydrazine group is very probable in the light of a recent structure determination of an adduct formed with a thiosemicarbazide (1960: 3).

**Platinum**

$PtCl_2 \cdot (CH_3)_2C=CHCOCH_3$ (1900: 2)

This compound should probably be excluded since $PtCl_2$ can form adducts with olefins which do not have functional groups but does *not* form adducts with saturated ketones. For a similar reason $PdCl_2$, $PdCl_4$, $PtCl_2$ and $PtCl_4$ adducts with amino acids and amino acid esters have been excluded. It seems probable that the energy of the Pt-N bond more than compensates for the loss of resonance energy which occurs when the amide group changes its structure to make the lone electron pair on the nitrogen available for adduct formation.

**Copper**

$2CuI \cdot CH_3CHO$ (1940: 4)
$3CuI \cdot C_3H_7CHO$ (1940: 4)

These two compounds, which have quite low dissociation pressures, together with some similar adducts of other monovalent copper salts, have compositions which offer an interesting challenge to the structural as well as to the theoretical chemist.

$CuCl_2 \cdot 2(CH_3)_2CO$ (1915: 3)
$CuCl_2 \cdot (CH_3)_2CO$ (1911: 2)
$Cu(CH_3COO)_2 \cdot CH_3COOH$ (1946: 2)
$CuCl_2 \cdot 2RCONH_2$ (1886: 1; 1960: 35)
$CuCl_2 \cdot C_6H_5CONH_2$ (1923: 2)
$Cu(HCONH)_2 \cdot 2HCONH_2$ (1910: 6)

This and similar adducts with Ni(II), Co(II) and Zn(II) are formed by decomposition reactions with formamide.

$CuCl_2 \cdot 2(NH_2)_2CO$ (1857: 1; 1957: 7)
$CuCl_2 \cdot 2NH_2CONHCONH_2$ (1898: 1)

This biuret adduct is not a molecule (1959: 25) but it is interesting to observe that only the oxygen atoms are used for adduct formation.

$CuCl_2 \cdot (C_6H_5)_3Sb=NCOCH_3$ (1954: 6)
Compare the corresponding $HgCl_2$ adduct.

**Silver**

$AgNO_3 \cdot CH_3CONH_2$ (1960: 42)

**Gold**

$AuCl_3 \cdot (C_6H_5)_2CO$ (1958: 26)
The aliphatic ketones are oxidized by $AuCl_3$.
$AuCl_3 \cdot C_6H_5COOH$ (1958: 26)

## 6. Adducts with acyl halides

**Magnesium**

$MgBr_2 \cdot C_6H_5COCl$ (1906: 2)

**Boron**

$BF_3 \cdot CH_3COF$ and similar adducts (1943: 1; 1956: 15; 1957: 9)

$BF_3 \cdot CH_3COCl$ and similar adducts (1932: 2; 1939: 5; 1943: 1)

$BCl_3 \cdot CH_3COCl$ (1956: 16)

This is an example of the surprising case of adduct formation established by a melting point maximum and at the same time showing positive deviations from Raoult's law. The corresponding $C_6H_5COCl$ adduct does not exist (1956: 16).

$BF_3 \cdot COCl_2$ (1949: 4)

**Aluminium**

$AlCl_3 \cdot CH_3COCl$ and similar adducts (1893: 1; 1900: 1; 1901: 1; 1902: 3; 1911: 3; 1913: 3; 1918: 1; 1932: 4; 1957: 8; 1961: 11)

$AlCl_3 \cdot CCl_2{=}CClCOCl$ (1913: 3)

The adduct with this completely chlorinated donor molecule has been described as a very stable compound with respect to irreversible decomposition.

$2AlX_3 \cdot C_6H_4(COCl)_2$ (1902: 3)

$AlCl_3 \cdot NH_2COCl$ (1948: 3)

This compound, whose structure is unknown, is claimed to be useful in the Gattermann synthesis of amides.

**Gallium**

$GaCl_3 \cdot CH_3COCl$ and similar adducts (1941: 1; 1956: 16; 1959: 26)

**Titanium**

$TiCl_4 \cdot CH_3COCl$ and similar adducts (1880: 2, 4; 1952: 5; 1958: 22; 1959: 10, 27; 1960: 29)

$2TiCl_4 \cdot (CH_3)_2C_6H_3COCl$ and similar adducts (1960: 29; 1961: 11,12)

It should be observed that PFEIFFER (1910: 5) could not find any corresponding $SnCl_4$ adducts.

**Antimony**

$SbCl_5 \cdot CH_3COCl$ and similar adducts (1902: 4; 1932: 2; 1944: 2; 1959: 27)

$2SbCl_5 \cdot 3C_6H_5COCl$ (1901: 2)

This is another example of a puzzling 2:3 adduct with $SbCl_5$. $SbCl_3$ does not form adducts with acyl halides (1912: 3).

**Manganese**

$MnCl_2 \cdot C_6H_5COCl$ (1959: 28)

**Iron**

$FeCl_3 \cdot C_6H_5COCl$ and similar adducts (1903: 4; 1959: 26)

## 7. Adducts with donor molecules containing the group ⩾NO

**Magnesium**

$MgBr(C_6H_5) \cdot C_6H_5(CH_3)_2NO$
and similar adducts (1948: 4)

**Zinc**

$ZnBr_2 \cdot 2C_6H_5(C_6H_5CH{=}CHCH{=})NO$ (1954: 10)
$ZnCl_2 \cdot 2C_5H_5NO$ (1961: 13)

**Boron**

$BF_3 \cdot (CH_3)_3NO$ (1945: 5; 1959: 29)

**Silicon**

$SiCl_4 \cdot x(CH_3)_3NO$ (1945: 5)

**Tin**

$SnCl_4 \cdot 2C_5H_5NO$ (1961: 13)

**Phosphorus**

$PCl_3 \cdot x(CH_3)_3NO$ (1945: 5)

**Sulfur**

$SO_2 \cdot (CH_3)_3NO$ (1943: 2; 1948: 5)
$SO_3 \cdot (CH_3)_3NO$ (1948: 5)

**Molybdenum**

$MoO_2Cl_2 \cdot 2C_5H_5NO$ (1962: 21)

**Manganese**

$MnBr_2 \cdot 2(CH_3)_3NO$ (1962: 16)

**Iron**

$FeCl_3 \cdot 2C_5H_5NO$ (1962: 16)

**Cobalt**

$CoBr_2 \cdot 2(CH_3)_3NO$ (1962: 16)

**Copper**

| | |
|---|---|
| $CuCl_2 \cdot 2C_5H_5NO$ | (1961: 13; 1962: 16) |
| $CuCl_2 \cdot C_5H_5NO$ | (1961: 13; 1962: 16) |

## 8. Adducts with donor molecules containing the group —$NO_2$

**Beryllium**

| | |
|---|---|
| $BeCl_2 \cdot 2C_6H_5NO_2$ | (1925: 3) |
| $BeCl_2 \cdot$ (naphthalene ring) —$NH_2$, $NO_2$ 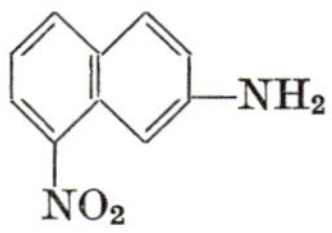 | (1947: 4) |

**Mercury**

| | |
|---|---|
| $HgCl_2 \cdot CH_3C_6H_4NO_2$ | (1909: 4) |

**Boron**

| | |
|---|---|
| $BCl_3 \cdot C_6H_5NO_2$ and similar adducts | (1956: 17) |

**Aluminium**

| | |
|---|---|
| $AlBr_3 \cdot 2CH_3NO_2$ | (1959: 30) |
| $AlCl_3 \cdot 2C_6H_5NO_2$ and similar adducts | (1910: 7) |
| $AlBr_3 \cdot CH_3NO_2$ and similar adducts | (1958: 14; 1959: 30; 1961: 14) |
| $AlCl_3 \cdot C_6H_5NO_2$ and similar adducts | (1893: 2; 1904: 5, 8; 1910: 4, 7; 1913: 4; 1932: 4; 1957: 10; 1958: 14; 1961: 21) |
| $AlBr_3 \cdot CH_3C_6H_4NO_2$(p) | (1958: 14) |

This and the corresponding nitrobenzene adduct both exist in two isomeric forms (1961: 21); the difference between them is not known.

| | |
|---|---|
| $AlCl_3 \cdot C_6H_4(NO_2)_2$(m) | (1904: 5) |

**Gallium**

| | |
|---|---|
| $GaCl_3 \cdot CH_3C_6H_4NO_2$(p) | (1941: 1) |

**Tin**

| | |
|---|---|
| $SnCl_4 \cdot C_6H_5NO_2$ and similar adducts | (1916: 1; 1927: 6; 1930: 5) |

It should be noted that no 1:2 adducts have been reported.

**Titanium**

| | |
|---|---|
| $TiF_4 \cdot C_6H_5NO_2$ | (1958: 22) |
| $TiCl_4 \cdot CH_3NO_2$ and similar adducts | (1927: 6) |
| $TiCl_4 \cdot C_6H_5NO_2$ and similar adducts | (1927: 6; 1934: 6; 1942: 1; 1957: 10; 1958: 22) |

There is no definite agreement about which adducts are formed with *meta* dinitrobenzene. Mole ratios 4:1, 3:2, 1:1, 2:3 and 1:2 have been suggested (1927: 6; 1932: 5; 1942: 1, 2).

**Antimony**

$SbCl_5 \cdot 2C_6H_5NO_2$ (1937: 3)
$2SbCl_5 \cdot 3C_6H_5NO_2$ (1901: 2)
$SbCl_5 \cdot C_6H_5NO_2$ and similar adducts (1937: 3; 1957: 10)
$SbCl_3 \cdot C_6H_5NO_2$ and similar adducts (1910: 8; 1912: 4)

Phase diagrams show that in many cases no adducts are formed with $SbCl_3$ (1948: 6, 7)

## 9. Adducts with donor molecules containing the group —N=O

No systematic studies have been made of nitroso compounds as donor molecules, but it is very probable that in the absence of atomic rearrangements further studies would be rewarding. The only definite example reported is:
$SnCl_4 \cdot 2C_6H_5NO$ (1927: 6)

## 10. Adducts with donor molecules containing the group $\geqslant P{=}O$

**Lithium**

$LiBr \cdot (C_6H_5)_3PO$ (1953: 7)
This is included only as an example of the formation of adduct molecules by salts of the alkali metals with donor molecules of this type.

**Magnesium**

$MgI(CH_3) \cdot 2(C_6H_5CH_2)_3PO$ (1906: 3)
$2MgCl_2 \cdot POCl_3$ (1903: 5)

It is remarkable that MgO and some other oxides also form adducts with $POCl_3$ (1912: 5). See also under manganese.

**Zinc**

$ZnI_2 \cdot 2(C_2H_5)_3PO$ and similar adducts (1861: 1; 1906: 3; 1952: 10; 1960: 11, 19)

**Cadmium**

$CdI_2 \cdot 2(C_6H_5)_3PO$ (1906: 3; 1960: 19)

**Mercury**

$HgCl_2 \cdot 3(C_6H_5CH_2)_3PO$ (1880: 3)
$HgCl_2 \cdot 2(C_6H_5)_3PO$ (1906: 3; 1959: 11)
$HgCl_2 \cdot (CH_3)_3PO$ and similar adducts (1959: 11)
$5HgCl_2 \cdot 2(CH_3)_3PO$ (1959: 11)
$HgCl(C_6H_5)$ and $Hg(C_6H_5)_2$ do not give adducts with $(CH_3)_3PO$ (1959: 11)
$3HgCl_2 \cdot N^+(CH_3)_3C_2H_4OPO(OH)O^-$ (1944: 5)

**Boron**

$BF_3 \cdot (CH_3)_3PO$ and similar adducts (1951: 10; 1960: 31)
$BH_3 \cdot H_3PO$ (1961: 22)

This remarkable donor molecule is described for the first time in this paper.
The adducts with different acids of phosphorus have compositions which show clearly that it is only the phosphoryl oxygen, as opposed to the bridging oxygen atoms, which functions as the donor. All such adducts are of importance as catalysts (1948: 8; 1957: 15).
$BF_3 \cdot (HO)_3PO$ (1948: 8; 1959: 31)
The deuterated adduct has also been prepared (1959: 31).
$2BF_3 \cdot H_4P_2O_7$ (1948: 8)
$BCl_3 \cdot (RO)_3PO$ (1959: 32; 1960: 31)
$BCl_3 \cdot (RO)_2POCl$ (1960: 31)
$BCl_3 \cdot ROPOCl_2$ (1960: 31)
$BF_3 \cdot POF_3$ (1943: 3)

The existence of this adduct is not firmly established.

$BF_3 \cdot POCl_3$ (1961: 22)
$BCl_3 \cdot POCl_3$ and similar adducts (1871: 1; 1903: 5; 1943: 4; 1960: 33, 43, 44; 1962: 15)

**Aluminium**

$AlI_3 \cdot 2POCl_3$ and similar adducts (1952: 11; 1957: 16; 1958: 27; 1959: 33)
$2AlCl_3 \cdot 3POCl_3$ (1959: 34)
$AlCl_3 \cdot POCl_3$ and similar adducts (1903: 5; 1952: 11; 1957: 16; 1958: 27)

**Gallium**

$GaCl_3 \cdot 2POCl_3$ (1957: 17)
$GaCl_3 \cdot POCl_3$ and similar adducts (1957: 17, 18; 1958: 28)

**Silicon**

$SiCl_4 \cdot 2(C_6H_5)_3PO$ and similar adducts (1962: 30)

**Tin**

$SnCl_4 \cdot 2(C_6H_5)_3PO$ and similar adducts (1958: 12)
$SnCl_4 \cdot 2(C_6H_5O)_3PO$ (1962: 31)
$SnCl_4 \cdot 2POCl_3$ and similar adducts (1929: 3; 1956: 18; 1958: 3, 12; 1961: 53)

The adducts $2SnCl_4 \cdot POCl_3$ (1903: 5) and $SnCl_4 \cdot POCl_3$ (1952: 11), claimed to exist, could not be found in phase equilibrium studies.
$SnOCl_2 \cdot 2POCl_3$ (1961: 23)
$SnCl_4 \cdot P_2O_3Cl_4$ (1959: 35)

This composition is taken as strong evidence that only phosphoryl oxygen atoms are donors.

**Titanium**

$TiCl_4 \cdot 2(C_6H_5)_3PO$ (1958: 12)
$TiCl_4 \cdot 2POCl_3$ and similar adducts (1903: 6; 1952: 11; 1953: 8; 1956: 18; 1958: 12; 1961: 53)
$TiCl_4 \cdot POCl_3$ (1867: 1; 1877: 1; 1953: 8; 1956: 18; 1958: 12; 1961: 53)
Three modifications of this adduct exist (1960:1)

**Zirconium**

$ZrCl_4 \cdot 2POCl_3$ (1952: 12; 1956: 19,20)
$ZrCl_4 \cdot POCl_3$ (1952: 12; 1956; 20)

Similar adducts have also been obtained with mixed oxide halides such as $POFCl_2$ (1952: 12).
In addition, another compound is described, and given two different formulae, $2ZrCl_4 \cdot POCl_3$ (1924: 6) or $3ZrCl_4 \cdot 2POCl_3$ (1949: 5). This compound would be of some importance since it can be separated from the corresponding $HfCl_4$ compound by fractional sublimation. It is most doubtful, however, whether it is a definite compound as opposed to an azeotropic mixture (1956: 21, 22.)

**Hafnium**

$HfCl_4 \cdot 2POCl_3$ (1952: 12; 1958: 29)
$HfCl_4 \cdot POCl_3$ (1952: 12; 1958: 29)

**Arsenic**

$AsCl_5 \cdot (CH_3)_3PO$ (1959: 11)

Arsenic pentachloride does not exist but can be stabilized by adduct formation with the strong donor molecule $(CH_3)_3PO$. It must be remembered, however, that the evidence for the existence of this adduct is not conclusive.
$AsCl_3 \cdot (CH_3)_3PO$ (1959: 11)
$AsCl_3 \cdot POCl_3$ (1958: 3; 1959: 10)

**Antimony**

$SbCl_5 \cdot (CH_3)_3PO$ and similar adducts (1959: 11)
$SbCl_3 \cdot 2(CH_3)_3PO$ (1959: 11)
$SbCl_3 \cdot (CH_3)_3PO$ (1959: 11)
$SbCl_5 \cdot POCl_3$ and similar adducts (1867: 1; 1903: 5; 1952: 11; 1958: 3; 1959: 36; 1962: 17)
$2SbCl_5 \cdot POCl_3$ (1959: 36)
$2SbCl_5 \cdot P_2O_3Cl_4$ (1959: 35)

See comment on the corresponding tin compound.

$SbCl_3 \cdot 2POCl_3$ (1959: 37)

**Bismuth**

$BiCl_3 \cdot 2POCl_3$ (1960: 23)

**Vanadium**

$VCl_3 \cdot 2R_3PO$ (1959: 32)

**Niobium**

$NbCl_5 \cdot POCl_3$ (1957: 32; 1959: 13,38)

**Tantalum**

$TaCl_5 \cdot POCl_3$ (1957: 32; 1959: 13,38)

**Sulfur**

$SO_3 \cdot (CH_3)_3PO$ and similar adducts (1951: 10; 1959: 11; 1961: 24)

**Selenium**

$SeOCl_2 \cdot (CH_3)_3PO$ (1959: 11)
$3SeOCl_2 \cdot 2POCl_3$ is considered to be a mixture of $3SeCl_4$ and $P_2O_5$, both insoluble in $SeOCl_2$ as well as in $POCl_3$ (1958: 3)

**Tellurium**

$TeCl_4 \cdot POCl_3$ (1908: 3; 1952: 11)

**Chromium**

$CrOCl \cdot POCl_3$ (1916: 2)

**Molybdenum**

$MoOCl_3 \cdot 2(C_6H_5)_3PO$ (1962: 21)
$MoO_2Cl_2 \cdot 2(C_6H_5)_3PO$ (1962: 21)
$MoCl_5 \cdot POCl_3$ (1879: 2)
Prepared from $MoO_3$ and $POCl_3$.
$6MoCl_2 \cdot 2(C_6H_5)_3PO$ (1961: 25)
This is probably a complex compound with the structure best described by the formula $(Mo_6Cl_8)Cl_4[(C_6H_5)_3PO]_2$

**Uranium**

$UO_2(NO_3)_2 \cdot 2(C_2H_5O)_3PO$ (1960: 10)
$UCl_4 \cdot 4POCl_3$ (1960: 45)
$UCl_4 \cdot POCl_3$ (1960: 45)

**Manganese**

$MnX_2 \cdot 2(C_6H_5)_3PO$ (1961: 3)
$MnO \cdot P_2O_3Cl_4 \cdot 2CH_3COOC_2H_5$ (1961: 26)

**Rhenium**

$ReCl_3 \cdot 2(C_6H_5)_3PO$ (1962: 24)

**Iron**

| | |
|---|---|
| $FeBr_2 \cdot 2(C_6H_5)_3PO$ | (1958: 12) |
| $2FeCl_3 \cdot 3(C_6H_5CH_2)_3PO$ | (1880: 3) |
| $FeBr_2 \cdot 2POBr_3$ | (1958: 12) |
| $2FeCl_3 \cdot 3POCl_3$ | (1955: 7) |
| $FeCl_3 \cdot POCl_3$ | (1955: 7; 1959: 34) |
| $2FeCl_3 \cdot POCl_3$ | (1904: 9) |

**Cobalt**

| | |
|---|---|
| $CoI_3 \cdot 3(C_6H_{11})_3PO$ | (1960: 12) |
| $CoCl_2 \cdot 3(C_6H_5CH_2)_3PO$ | (1880: 3) |
| $CoCl_2 \cdot 2(C_6H_5)_3PO$ and similar adducts | (1906: 3; 1960: 11, 12, 19) |

**Nickel**

| | |
|---|---|
| $NiBr_2 \cdot 2(C_6H_5)_3PO$ and similar adducts | (1960: 11, 12, 14; 1961: 27) |

**Palladium**

| | |
|---|---|
| $PdCl_2 \cdot 3(C_6H_5CH_2)_3PO$ | (1880: 3) |

**Platinum**

| | |
|---|---|
| $PtCl_4 \cdot 3(C_6H_5CH_2)_3PO$ | (1880: 3) |
| $PtBr_4 \cdot 2(C_2H_5O)_3PO$ | (1905: 2) |
| $PtCl_4 \cdot (C_2H_5O)_3PO$ | (1903: 7) |

**Copper**

| | |
|---|---|
| $CuSO_4 \cdot 3(C_2H_5)_3PO$ | (1862: 1) |
| $CuCl_2 \cdot 2(C_6H_5)_3PO$ and similar adducts | (1960: 11; 1961: 4) |
| $CuCl_2 \cdot (C_2H_5)_3PO$ and similar adducts | (1906: 3; 1961: 4) |

## 11. Adducts with donor molecules containing the group $\geqslant As{=}O$

**Mercury**

| | |
|---|---|
| $HgCl_2 \cdot 2(C_6H_5)_3AsO$ | (1961: 16) |
| $HgCl_2 \cdot (C_6H_5)_3AsO$ | (1961: 16) |
| $2HgCl_2 \cdot (C_3H_7)_3AsO$ | (1899: 1) |

**Tin**

| | |
|---|---|
| $SnCl_4 \cdot 2(C_6H_5)_3AsO$ and similar adducts | (1961: 16) |

**Antimony**

| | |
|---|---|
| $SbCl_5 \cdot (C_6H_5)_3AsO$ | (1961: 16) |
| $SbCl_3 \cdot 2(C_6H_5)_3AsO$ | (1961: 16) |

**Sulfur**

| | |
|---|---|
| $SO_3 \cdot (C_6H_5)_3AsO$ and similar adducts | (1961: 24) |

**Molybdenum**

| | |
|---|---|
| $MoCl_5 \cdot (C_6H_5)_3AsO$ | (1962: 21) |
| $MoOCl_3 \cdot 2(C_6H_5)_3AsO$ | (1962: 21) |
| $MoO_2Cl_2 \cdot 2(C_6H_5)_3AsO$ | (1962: 21) |
| $MoOCl_3 \cdot (C_6H_5)_3 AsO \cdot (CH_3)_2CO$ | (1962: 21) |
| $3MoCl_2 \cdot (C_6H_5)_3AsO$ | (1961: 25) |

See the corresponding phosphine oxide adduct.

**Manganese**

$MnCl_2 \cdot 2(C_6H_5)_3AsO$ (1961: 3, 16)

**Rhenium**

$ReCl_3 \cdot 2(C_6H_5)_3AsO$ (1962: 24)

**Iron**

$FeCl_3 \cdot 2(C_6H_5)_3AsO$ (1961: 16)

**Cobalt**

$CoCl_2 \cdot 2(C_6H_5)_3AsO$ and similar adducts (1961: 16)

**Nickel**

$NiCl_2 \cdot 2(C_6H_5)_3AsO$ and similar adducts (1960: 15; 1961: 16,27)

**Copper**

$CuCl_2 \cdot 2(C_6H_5)_3AsO$ and similar adducts (1961: 4)

## 12. Adducts with donor molecules containing the group >Sb=O

$SO_3 \cdot (C_6H_5)_3SbO$ (1961: 24)

## 13. Adducts with donor molecules containing the group >S=O

**Zinc**

| | |
|---|---|
| $ZnCl_2 \cdot 2(CH_3)_2SO$ | (1960: 16) |
| $ZnBr_2 \cdot (CH_3)_2SO$ | (1960: 16) |

**Cadmium**

$CdCl_2 \cdot (CH_3)_2SO$ and similar adducts (1960: 16)

**Mercury**

| | |
|---|---|
| $Hg(SCN)_2 \cdot 2(CH_3)_2SO$ | (1960: 17) |
| $HgCl_2 \cdot (CH_3)_2SO$ | (1961: 5) |
| $2HgCl_2 \cdot (CH_3)_2SO$ | (1960: 16) |
| $3HgBr_2 \cdot (CH_3)_2SO$ | (1960: 16) |

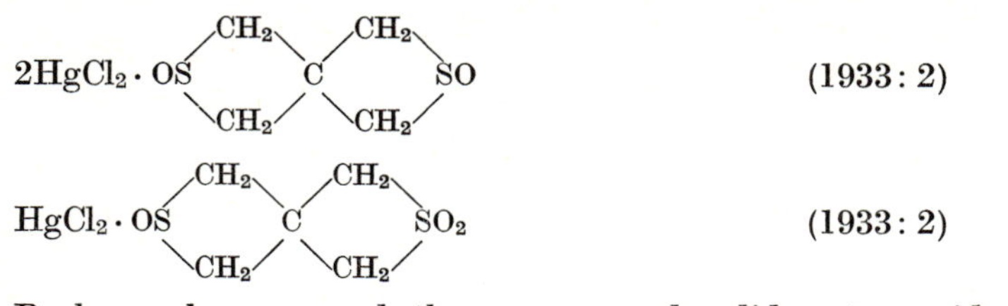


Backer, who prepared these compounds, did not consider them to be donor-acceptor compounds but his structure proposals do not seem very probable in the light of present day knowledge.

**Boron**

$BF_3 \cdot (CH_3)_2SO$ and similar adducts (1960: 16, 46)
$BCl_3 \cdot (C_6H_5)_2SO$ (1961: 28)

The corresponding $(CH_3)_2SO$ adduct undergoes a rearrangement (1961: 28)
$BF_3 \cdot SOF_2$ (1943: 3)

The corresponding $SOCl_2$ adduct does not exist.

$3BF_3 \cdot 2[N(CH_3)_2]_2SO$ (1954: 11)
$BF_3 \cdot CH_3N{=}SO$ (1954: 11)

The last two compounds are probably adducts with the nitrogen atoms of the donor molecules but the coordination is not known with certainty.

**Aluminium**

$2AlCl_3 \cdot SOCl_2$ (1947: 5)

**Silicon**

$SiF_4 \cdot 2(CH_3)_2SO$ (1959: 39; 1960: 28)
See, however, remarks in (1961: 28).

**Germanium**

$GeF_4 \cdot 2(CH_3)_2SO$ (1960: 28)

**Tin**

$SnF_4 \cdot 2(CH_3)_2SO$ (1960: 28)
$SnCl_4 \cdot 2(CH_3)_2SO$ and similar adducts (1960: 16; 1961: 28)
$SnCl_4$ does not form adducts with $SOCl_2$ (1932: 6; 1959: 10)

**Lead**

$PbX_2 \cdot (CH_3)_2SO$ (1961: 5)

**Titanium**

$TiF_4 \cdot 2(CH_3)_2SO$ (1960: 28)

**Zirconium**

$ZrF_4 \cdot 2(CH_3)_2SO$ (1960: 28)
$ZrCl_4 \cdot SOCl_2$ (1947: 6; 1956: 19)

**Antimony**

$SbCl_5 \cdot (CH_3)_2SO$ and similar adducts (1959: 37)
$SbCl_3 \cdot 2(CH_3)_2SO$ (1959: 37)
$SbCl_5 \cdot SOCl_2$ (1959: 37)

**Chromium**

$CrCl_3 \cdot 3(CH_3)_2SO$ (1960: 16)

**Molybdenum**

$MoOCl_3 \cdot 2(CH_3)_2SO$ (1962: 21)
$MoO_2Cl_2 \cdot 2(CH_3)_2SO$ (1962: 21)
$MoF_4 \cdot 2(CH_3)_2SO$ (1960: 28)

**Uranium**

$UO_2(NO_3)_2 \cdot 2(CH_3)_2SO$ (1960: 16)
$UCl_5 \cdot SOCl_2$ (1947: 6; 1957: 19)

**Manganese**

$MnCl_2 \cdot 3(CH_3)_2SO$ (1960: 16, 17, 47; 1961: 29)
$MnBr_2 \cdot 2(CH_3)_2SO$ (1960: 16)

**Cobalt**

$CoCl_2 \cdot 3(CH_3)_2SO$ and similar adducts (1960: 16, 17, 47; 1961: 5, 29)

**Iron**

$FeCl_3 \cdot 2(CH_3)_2SO$ (1960: 16; 1961: 5)
$FeCl_3 \cdot (CH_3C_6H_4)_2SO$ (1907: 5)

**Nickel**

$NiCl_2 \cdot 3(CH_3)_2SO$ and similar adducts (1960: 17, 17, 47; 1961: 5, 29)

**Palladium**

$PdCl_2 \cdot 2(CH_3)_2SO$ (1960: 16; 1961: 5)
This has been suggested as a case of adduct formation with sulfur (p. 15).

**Copper**

$CuBr_2 \cdot 3(CH_3)_2SO$ (1960: 16, 47; 1961: 29)
$CuCl_2 \cdot 2(CH_3)_2SO$ and similar adducts (1960: 16, 17, 47; 1961: 5, 29)
$CuCl_2 \cdot (CH_3)_2SO$ (1961: 5)

## 14. Adducts with donor molecules containing the group $>S\ll^{O}_{O}$

**Boron**

$BF_3 \cdot CH_3(C_{12}H_{25})SO_2$ (1960: 46)
$BF_3 \cdot [N(CH_3)_2]_2SO_2$ (1954: 11)
See comments under the corresponding sulfoxide adduct.

**Aluminium**

$AlCl_3 \cdot (C_6H_5)_2SO_2$ and similar adducts (1900: 1; 1918: 2)
$AlCl_3 \cdot CH_3SO_2Cl$ and similar adducts (1900: 1, 3; 1913: 3; 1914: 3; 1916: 3; 1918: 2)
$AlCl_3 \cdot C_6H_5SO_2NH_2$ (1958: 30)
Here nitrogen is probably the donor atom, but some further studies are needed.

**Tin**

$SnCl_4 \cdot (CH_3)_2SO_2$ (1962: 18)
$SnCl_4 \cdot (CH_3)(CH_3O)\ SO_2$ (1962: 31)
It should be observed that both these compounds are 1 : 1 adducts

**Titanium**

$TiCl_4 \cdot CH_3C_6H_4SO_2NH_2$ (1934: 4)
See the corresponding $AlCl_3$ adduct
$TiCl_4 \cdot 2SO_2Cl_2$ (1937: 4)
The melting point, — 43.75°, is in agreement with a very weak donor-acceptor interaction, but the original paper has another structure suggestion.

**Phosphorus**

$PCl_3 \cdot NH_2SO_2Cl$ (1910: 9)
This compound is reported to be remarkably stable and is probably not a molecular adduct.

**Antimony**

$SbCl_5 \cdot (CH_3)_2SO_2$ and similar adducts (1959: 37)
$SbCl_3 \cdot (CH_3)_2SO_2$ (1959: 37)
$SbCl_3$ does not form an adduct with $C_6H_5SO_2(OH)$ (1912: 6)
$SbCl_5 \cdot SO_2Cl_2$ (1959: 37)

**Cobalt**

$CoCl_2 \cdot$ (cyclic $CH_2—CH_2$, $SO_2$, $CH_2—CH_2$ ring: sulfolane) (1962: 22)

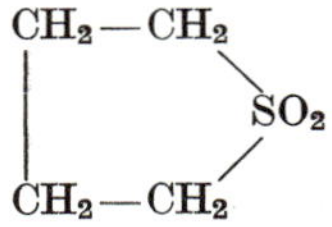

```
        CH2—CH2
        |       \
CoCl2 · |        SO2
        |       /
        CH2—CH2
```

## 15. Adducts with sulfur dioxide and sulfur trioxide

These oxides have been included here because their adducts provide a large number of structural problems. In some cases molecular adducts may form, and in others atomic rearrangements may occur; the whole field is open to further investigation. Similar adducts can be obtained with other non-metal oxides, and $BF_3$ adducts with nitrogen oxides can be mentioned as an example (1955: 8; 1957: 20; 1958: 31). The sulfur oxides, however, have been much more extensively studied.

**Zinc**

$ZnCl_2 \cdot SO_3$ (1939: 6)

**Cadmium**

$CdCl_2 \cdot 2SO_3$ (1939: 6)

**Boron**

$BF_3 \cdot SO_2$ (1942: 3)
No $SO_2$ adduct is formed with $BCl_3$ (1945: 6)
$BCl_3 \cdot 2SO_3$ (1942: 4)

**Aluminium**

$AlCl_3 \cdot SO_2$ (1922: 2; 1942: 5)
The molecular structure suggested is very interesting:

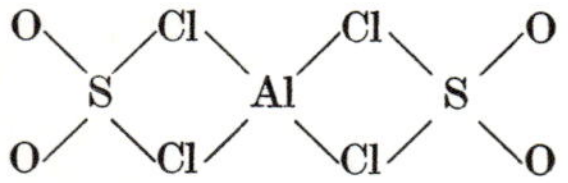

```
O      Cl       Cl      O
 \    /  \     /  \    /
  S       Al        S
 /    \  /     \  /    \
O      Cl       Cl      O
```

(1942: 5) but needs further confirmation.

$Al(C_2H_5)_3 \cdot 3SO_2$ (1953: 9)
This compound is suggested to be $Al(O_2SC_6H_5)_3$.

**Silicon**

$SiCl_4 \cdot SO_3$ (1942: 4)

**Tin**

$SnCl_4 \cdot 2SO_3$ (1937: 5; 1939: 6)
$2SnBr_4 \cdot SO_2$ (1945: 7)

**Titanium**

$TiCl_4 \cdot 2SO_3$ (1936: 6; 1949: 6)
$2TiCl_4 \cdot SO_2$ and similar adducts (1945: 7)

**Zirconium**

$ZrCl_4 \cdot SO_2$ (1929: 4)

**Antimony**

$SbCl_5 \cdot 2SO_3$ (1937: 5)
$SbCl_5 \cdot SO_3$ (1937: 5)

$SbF_5 \cdot SO_2$ (1951: 11)
$SbCl_3 \cdot 3SO_3$ (1938: 6)
$SbCl_3 \cdot 2SO_3$ (1938: 6)

**Bismuth**

$BiCl_3 \cdot 2SO_3$ (1938: 6)
$BiCl_3 \cdot SO_3$ (1938: 6)

**Uranium**

$UO_2Cl_2 \cdot 2SO_3$ (1939: 6)

**Cobalt**

$CoCl_2 \cdot 2SO_3$ (1939: 6)

**Nickel**

$NiCl_2 \cdot 4SO_3$ (1939: 6)

**Copper**

$CuCl_2 \cdot 4SO_3$ (1939: 6)

## 16. Adducts with donor molecules containing the >Se=O group

**Mercury**

$HgCl_2 \cdot R_2SeO$ (1951: 4)
See comment on p. 16

**Boron**

$2BCl_3 \cdot 3SeOCl_2$ (1961: 30)
This "compound" is probably a mixture of $B_2O_3$ and $SeCl_4$.

**Aluminium**

$2AlCl_3 \cdot 3SeOCl_2$ (1961: 30)
This is probably also a mixture.

**Tin**

$SnCl_4 \cdot 2SeOCl_2$ (1865: 1; 1923: 6; 1958: 3; 1959: 10)

**Titanium**

$TiCl_4 \cdot 2SeOCl_2$ (1865: 1; 1923: 6)

**Zirconium**

$ZrCl_4 \cdot 2SeOCl_2$ (1956: 19)

**Arsenic**

$AsCl_3$ does not form an adduct with $SeOCl_2$ (1959: 10; 1958: 3)

**Antimony**

$SbCl_5 \cdot SeOCl_2$ (1865: 1; 1958: 3)
The formula $SbCl_5 \cdot 2SeOCl_2$ quoted in (1923: 6) is probably a misprint.

**Iron**

$FeCl_3 \cdot 2SeOCl_2$ (1923: 6; 1956: 19)

## 17. Adducts with Brönsted acids

A Brönsted acid can never be a true Lewis acid, and something will be said about the differences which occur in their reactions with typical donor molecules which are both Lewis and Brönsted bases. The ability to add protons (the Brönsted definition of a base) always occurs in parallel with the existence of a lone electron pair (the Lewis definition) but the donation of a proton (Brönsted acid) is not quite analogous to the acceptance of an electron pair (Lewis acid).

In this connection there are two differences, which will be discussed briefly below. The formation of a hydrogen bond can be described formally as corresponding to a donor-acceptor reaction. The hydrogen atom in the acid HA increases its coordination from one to two according to the formula AH . . .D. Theoretically, however, a hydrogen atom cannot form more than one electron pair bond, and different attempts have been made to interpret the nature of the hydrogen bond without violating this basic theoretical condition. The present situation seems to be that the hydrogen bond is considered as originating mainly in the interaction of the electrostatic forces between acid and base, but that delocalization of electrons must also be taken into account. According to this it seems reasonable to include the Brönsted acids among the acceptor molecules with hydrogen representing the acceptor atom.

There is, however, a further complication, in that proton transfer occurs to a considerable degree so that ions are formed, and the stronger the hydrogen bond the easier is the proton transfer. With weak acids proton transfer is inappreciable and similar minor dissociation processes occur in many donor-acceptor systems, as will be discussed later.

In considering a solid adduct formed between a Brönsted acid and a donor molecule it is necessary to observe the same distinction as is made for donor-acceptor molecules in general, namely that between molecular adducts (with hydrogen bonds of the type AH . . . D) and salts (which also might contain hydrogen bonds of the type $A^- \ldots HD^+$).

The number of adducts formed between Brönsted acids and donor molecules is very large and the literature will not be covered here. Some important types of adducts will, however, be demonstrated and briefly exemplified. Adduct formation occurs mainly with strong acids such as $HNO_3$ and HCl, but weak acids can also form adducts with strong donors. Special importance is attached to the complex acids formed by reaction between Lewis acids and Brönsted acids, such as $SbCl_5 + HCl = HSbCl_6$ and $AuCl_3 + HCl = HAuCl_4$. These acids are all very strong and many of their adducts have been described. The following list gives some selected examples:

| | |
|---|---|
| $H_3PO_4 \cdot C_6H_5COCH_3$ | (1898: 2) |
| $HNO_3 \cdot (C_2H_5)_2CO$ | (1910: 2) |
| $HSbCl_6 \cdot 2RCOOR'$ | (1959: 22) |
| $HSbCl_6 \cdot RCOOR'$ | (1956: 23) |
| $HSbCl_6 \cdot 2RNO_2$ | (1956: 24) |
| $CCl_3COOH \cdot (CH_3)_3PO$ | (1906: 3) |
| $H_4Fe(CN)_6 \cdot 2(CH_3)_3PO$ | (1906: 3) |
| $HAuCl_4 \cdot 2(CH_3)_3PO$ | (1906: 3) |
| $HBiI_4 \cdot 2(CH_3)_3PO$ | (1906: 3) |
| $HHgI_3 \cdot 2(C_3H_7)_3PO$ | (1906: 3) |
| $H_2PtCl_6 \cdot 4(CH_3)_3PO$ | (1906: 3) |
| $H_2PtCl_6 \cdot 6(C_6H_5CH_2)_3PO$ | (1906: 3) |
| $HCl \cdot (C_6H_5)_3PO$ | (1906: 3) |
| $H_2Cr_2O_7 \cdot 2(CH_3)_3PO$ | (1906: 3) |
| $HSbCl_6 \cdot R_2SO_2$ | (1956: 24) |

The large number of phosphine oxide adducts have been presented in detail since they demonstrate a very interesting problem in connection with adducts of this type. Many of them contain two donor molecules for each available hydrogen atom, and this raises a query as to the character of the hydrogen bonds which are present. Do they contain symmetrical O—H—O bonds, and is this only possible with strong donors like phosphine oxides? A detailed study would probably reveal many interesting facts of a related nature.

The "onium" character of these adducts is still more obvious if in the complex acids hydrogen is replaced by alkyl groups. Thus it has been shown that not only $HSbCl_6 \cdot RR'CO$ but also $CH_3SbCl_6 \cdot RR'CO$ can be prepared, and it seems obvious that the latter contains the onium ion $CH_3RR'CO^+$ (1959: 22).

A remarkable class of adducts with Brönsted acids has recently been studied, namely that formed with the complicated acid $H_2[(Mo_6Cl_8)Cl_6]$. The adducts prepared are of the type 1:4 and 1:6 with $(C_6H_5)_3PO$, and 1:4 and 1:2 with $(C_6H_5)_3AsO$, (1961: 25).

## 18. Ternary adducts with carboxylic acids

When carboxylic acids function as *donor* molecules their acidity is influenced by adduct formation. The detailed nature of this interaction will be discussed more fully later and for present purposes it is sufficient to say that the acceptor atom attracts electrons first from the oxygen atom of the C = O bond in the carboxyl group $—C\langle^{OH}_{O}$, then from the carbon atom, and finally from the bridging oxygen. The extent of this electron attraction is increased by delocalization effects (see discussion on p. 90) and the net result of adduct formation is an increase in the acidity of the carboxylic acid. This was clearly understood and interpreted by MEERWEIN (1927: 2) in his studies of adducts between acetic acid and $ZnCl_2$ or $BF_3$. He found that the adduct formed with $ZnCl_2$ was an acid with a strength similar to that of sulfuric acid, and many other examples of this effect have since been studied.

It has been assumed that the increased acidity is responsible for the formation of compounds such as $SnCl_4 \cdot 2CH_3COOH \cdot C_6H_5COOH$ (1957: 21). In this and some related adducts (1956: 25, 26; 1957: 22) the acidity of the coordinated weak acid is assumed to increase sufficiently to permit proton transfer to, or strong hydrogen bond formation with, the third acid molecule which is a very weak base. (Cf. also $SnCl_4 \cdot 2CH_3COOH \cdot 2C_5H_5N$ (1960: 48).) Although the validity of this picture has not been definitely established the suggestion is reasonable, and it would be interesting to have further systematic studies of ternary adducts of this type.

It is clear that many of the loose addition compounds mentioned in the formal classification (p. 3) might also be adducts of this type. They differ only in that the extra molecule is of the same type as the one or more molecules which are bonded by donor-acceptor bonds. Typical examples are the 1:2 adducts between $BF_3$ and carboxylic acids, such as $BF_3 \cdot 2HCOOH$ (1931: 1; 1934: 3), or the 1:3 and 1:4 adducts between $SnCl_4$ and carboxylic acids (1930: 6; 1947: 3). The fact that no corresponding adducts with esters have been reported supports this interpretation.

Dipole moment studies of adducts $SnCl_4 \cdot 3RCOOH$ also give clear indication that the third donor molecule is added in a way different from that of the other two (1957: 23). (Cf. finally the results of viscosity studies, p. 52).

## 19. Other ternary adducts

No systematic studies seem to have been made of ternary systems containing either two different acceptors and one donor, or two different donors and one acceptor. Ternary compounds occurring in such systems are in general unlikely to be molecular adducts. The formation of ternary adducts would be favoured, however, by an exchange of halide ions and donor molecules yielding ionic compounds.

One example is the compound $SbCl_5 \cdot TiCl_4 \cdot 3POCl_3$ which is formed by reaction between $SbCl_5 \cdot POCl_3$ and $TiCl_4 \cdot 2POCl_3$ (1960: 49). Both these adducts are saturated with respect to donor-acceptor bonds; the acceptor atoms cannot increase their coordinations further and all possible donor atoms have been used. An exchange can take place, however, according to the equation: $SbCl_5 \cdot POCl_3 + TiCl_4 \cdot 2POCl_3 = SbCl_6^- + TiCl_3(POCl_3)_3^+$.

This suggestion has been supported by measurements of the conductivities of solutions in ethylene chloride, but conclusive evidence is still lacking.

[By comparison it may be mentioned that the compound $KCl \cdot TiCl_4 \cdot POCl_3$ reacts in $POCl_3$ as a binary electrolyte containing $K^+$ and $TiCl_5(POCl_3)^-$ ions (1961: 31)].

No corresponding ternary compounds are obtained in the systems $SbCl_5$—$SnCl_4$—$POCl_3$ and $SbCl_5$—$AsCl_3$—$POCl_3$ (1960: 49). The greater tendency of $TiCl_4$ to act as a chloride ion donor in these systems is in agreement with the active base strength of this compound as determined by potentiometric measurements (1958: 32).

The ternary compound $SbCl_5 \cdot ZrCl_4 \cdot 2POCl_3$ (1956: 19) is of special interest since by analogy it should contain a $ZrCl_3(POCl_3)_2^-$ ion which might be dimeric.

The compounds $SbCl_5 \cdot AlCl_3 \cdot 3POCl_3$ and $SnCl_4 \cdot 2AlCl_3 \cdot 2POCl_3$ (1952: 13) cannot easily be interpreted as ionic adducts and should be studied further, but $3SbCl_5 \cdot AlCl_3 \cdot 6POCl_3$ (1961: 32) fits the picture well and can be written $[Al(POCl_3)_6]\ (SbCl_6)_3$.

The adduct $SbCl_5 \cdot CH_3COCl \cdot$ [p-benzoquinone structure: O= ring =O] and the corresponding $SnCl_4$ adduct formed with two of each type of donor molecule are of special interest in the catalytical splitting of ethers, although it is probable that the interpretation of these compounds given in the original paper needs modifying (1932: 2).

## 20. Adduct molecules in the liquid state and in solution

The preceding systematic treatment and the later survey of structural studies (p. 63) deal mainly with pure adduct molecules as solids, or in some cases as liquids. At this point a brief review will be given of attempts to prove the existence of adduct molecules in the liquid state and in solution. The treatment is not complete; many investigations have led to very uncertain results, and as a rule only adducts which have also been isolated as solids will be considered.

### a) Molecular weight determinations

Extensive use has been made of the classical cryoscopic and ebullioscopic methods. (Vapour pressure studies have so far been of little use, even where they indicate adduct formation (1958: 33; 1959: 40)). However, most investigators have paid little attention to possible variations in the activity factors, and the detailed results are often inconclusive. In general, therefore, these investigations have done no more than show whether the adduct isolated and analyzed as a solid, also exists in the solution, or is more or less dissociated into its components. Many references to such studies are found in the systematic section, and few will be discussed in detail here. (Some quantitative results from dissociation studies will be mentioned in connection with the affinity studies (p. 59)). If, however, dissociation has led to unexpected intermediates of unknown constitution, or if association rather than dissociation has been found, the results will be discussed below.

The dissociation of 1:2 adducts is of particular interest in this connection. In the earlier discussion it was assumed that in these compounds acceptor atoms such as tin, titanium, zirconium and hafnium have octahedral coordination, and it was indicated that this coordination might also be preserved in 1:1 adducts by some kind of polymerization. Clearly molecular weight studies in suitable solvents should give further information on this point. The difficulty is, however, to find a suitable solvent. If the solvent possesses any kind of donor property, there is always the possibility that the apparent monomer $SnCl_4 \cdot D$ in which five-fold coordination occurs, in fact possesses octahedral coordination and contains an additional molecule of the solvent. For this reason nitrobenzene is not a good solvent, and even benzene might form an adduct as is shown by the isolation of solid ternary adducts $ZrCl_4 \cdot$ Ester·Benzene (1959: 41). Aliphatic chlorides and bromides would seem to be the most suitable solvents in this respect. At present, however, it cannot be claimed that the existence of isolated monomeric 1:1 adducts of $SnCl_4$, $TiCl_4$, $ZrCl_4$ and $HfCl_4$ has really been proved beyond doubt. The evidence is fairly convincing, nevertheless, and some of the most noteworthy results will now be mentioned.

The following instances in which 1:1 adducts of this type may possibly exist have been reported: $SnCl_4$ with esters (1924: 4) in $C_2H_4Br_2$ and with ketones (1932: 7) in $C_6H_6$, $TiCl_4$ with esters (1955: 9) in $C_6H_6$ and with $POCl_3$ in $C_6H_5NO_2$ (1960: 50), $ZrCl_4$ with esters in $C_6H_6$ (1959: 41), and with $POCl_3$ in $C_6H_5NO_2$ (1955: 10), $ZrBr_4$ with esters (1959: 20) and $ZrI_4$ with esters (1959: 42).

In a few cases dimeric molecules have also been found as in the compounds $TiCl_4 \cdot$Ester (partial association) (1955: 9) and $ZrCl_4 \cdot$Ester (1959: 19) (the proposed structure is rather improbable, however).

Very different types of association are also encountered. Thus the 1:1 adducts of $SnCl_4$ with dicarboxylic esters (1924: 4), (1959: 44), (1960: 39) and quinones (1960: 39) are dimeric and the probable structure of one such dimer can be written

$$\begin{array}{ccc} & O=C_6H_4=O & \\ Cl_4Sn & & SnCl_4 \\ & O=C_6H_4=O & \end{array}$$

while similar structures can be quoted for the diesters.

It is much more difficult to suggest a structure for the many dimers of $AlX_3 \cdot D$ adducts which have been identified, for example $AlCl_3 \cdot (C_6H_5)_2CO$ in $C_6H_6$ (1931: 3), $AlCl_3 \cdot C_6H_5COCl$ in $C_6H_6$ (1931: 3), $AlCl_3 \cdot CH_3CONH_2$ in $C_6H_5NO_2$ (1959: 43) and similar $AlBr_3$ adducts in $CS_2$ (1900: 3). The compound $AlCl_3 \cdot C_6H_5NO_2$ is also reported to be dimeric in $C_6H_6$ (1931: 3) whereas it has been suggested, rather surprisingly, that $AlCl_3$ should be monomeric in $C_6H_5NO_2$ (1951: 12). (Another surprising result is that $AlBr_3$ and $CH_3NO_2$ apparently form a 1:2 adduct in $C_2H_5Br$ but a 1:1 adduct in $C_6H_6$ (1959: 30).) The same kind of structural problem is associated with the polymerization of $FeCl_3 \cdot POCl_3$ in $C_6H_5NO_2$ (1955: 7). (Cf. also p. 56). One possible explanation lies in the development in these compounds of a coordination number higher than four together with some kind of bridge structure. Reports of the polymerization of $ZrCl_4 \cdot 2D$ adducts (1959:41) make this solution less probable, however, since in polymers of this type zirconium would obviously require a coordination number greater than six. Although not impossible, until structure determinations have been carried out, all this is mere conjecture.

Finally, something should be said about the results of extraction studies. When they are done carefully and analysed logically, such experiments give evidence concerning the molecular species which exist in different solvents. The literature is very rich in this field, particularly as regards lanthanide and actinide compounds, and only a few examples are quoted to indicate the kind of result that has been reported. Thus, in different extraction experiments, reasonable evidence has been obtained for the existence of the probable adduct molecules $ZrCl_4 \cdot 2(C_4H_9O)_3PO$ (1956: 27), $CoCl_2 \cdot 2(C_4H_9O)_3PO$ (1959: 45), $UO_2(NO_3)_2 \cdot 2CH_3(C_5H_{11}O)_2PO$ (1960: 51). Similar zirconium adducts have been demonstrated in amide extraction experiments (1960: 52).

## b) Viscosity

Viscosity as a function of compound formation in binary systems of donor and acceptor molecules was first studied by Kurnakov. He pointed out that the mere presence of a maximum in a viscosity isotherm cannot be accepted as proof of compound formation. Flat maxima are often situated at irrational compositions and in addition their positions are influenced by changes of temperature. Kurnakov therefore drew a distinction between these and the "rational" maxima which are discontinous at the maximum point (two curves with different derivatives cross at a singular point) (1913: 5; 1946: 3) (Fig. 5).

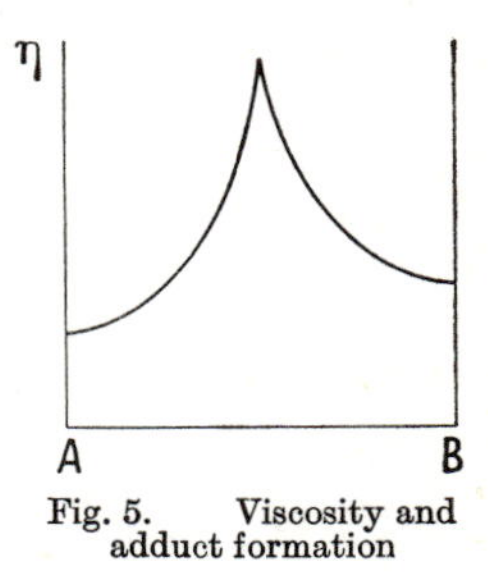

Fig. 5. Viscosity and adduct formation

In the first references to the application of these ideas to donor-acceptor adducts, there are already examples which show that only the "rational" maxima are in agreement with the melting point maxima (and are often more sharply defined), while flat maxima give more ambiguous information.

It has since been demonstrated that a singular point need not be a maximum, but might be any discontinous break in a viscosity isotherm (1946: 4). The factors which govern the shape of "flat" maxima have also been discussed (1946: 5). The difference between the two types of viscosity isotherm has been extensively discussed by Ewell, who states explicitly that only "rational" maxima can be taken as proof of adduct formation (1937: 6). In the following discussion, some results based on "rational" viscosity maxima will be mentioned, with additional references to some less reliable attempts to account for flat maxima.

The formation of a number of 1:2 adducts of $SnCl_4$ with esters of aliphatic acids has been established in this way, while the system with ethyl benzoate which contains two adducts (1:1 and 1:2) shows a flat maximum at a point intermediate between these two compositions (1923: 4; 1924: 5; 1938: 3, 7; 1959: 46). A more surprising result has been obtained in studies of systems of $SnCl_4$ with carboxylic acids. The viscosity isotherm gives definite indication that the compound $SnCl_4 \cdot 3CH_3COOH$ is present in the melt (1927: 7; 1947: 3). Similar evidence has been obtained for the compound $SnCl_4 \cdot 2CH_3COOH \cdot C_6H_5COOH$ (1957: 21). (Cf. other evidence for compounds of this type on p. 48). Caution must be recommended, however, in the interpretation of results for systems in which the viscosity increases rapidly as a result of small additions of one component. The possibility cannot be ignored that very high and sharp maxima might occur simply because of changes in the structure of the liquid, even in the absence of definite adduct formation.

The studies of $TiCl_4$ adducts with different esters have yielded rather interesting results. Thus almost undissociated $TiCl_4 \cdot 2HCOOC_2H_5$ has been proved to exist in the melt (1954: 12) while in all other cases (with larger ester molecules) it has only been possible to establish the existence of 1:1 adducts. (1955: 11; 1956: 28, 29). The authors, however, interpret the changed shape of the viscosity isotherms at higher temperatures as being due to the coexistence of 1:2 adducts (1956: 28). This probably sets (or passes) the limit of reliability for conclusions based on viscosity measurements. A considerable number of systems with flat maxima or no maxima at all have been studied by Usanovich and Sumarokova, but not all the references are quoted here.

Some negative results are also of interest. Thus it has been found that although $SbBr_3$ gives adducts with most ketones, none is formed with acetone (1924: 5). Nor has it been possible to detect any interaction between $SiCl_4$ and $CH_3COOC_2H_5$, $(C_6H_5)_2CO$ or $C_6H_5NO_2$ (1957: 24) or between $GeCl_4$ and $CH_3COOC_2H_5$ (1957: 25).

Of more fundamental interest is the determination of the activation energy of viscous flow for the melts of well defined addition compounds. Accurate data have been presented for $BF_3 \cdot CH_3COOH$ (1951: 13), $BF_3 \cdot CH_3COOR$ (1952: 4; 1953: 3), $GaCl_3 \cdot POCl_3$ (1957: 17) and $GaBr_3 \cdot POBr_3$ (1958: 28). (In many of the earlier references data are available which permit the calculation of at least approximate activation energies of migration.) A combination of the viscosity results with specific volume data permits the calculation of Batschinski's constant, which is a measure of the size of the "flow units". The results in the preceding references give clear indications of a considerable increase in the size of this unit as a result of adduct formation.

Finally, mention should be made of an interesting effect observed during these studies. On passing from the stable melt to the supercooled melt (supercooling is very common in these systems) the activation energy of viscous flow shows a discontinuity. The activation energy of migration is thus always lower for the normal than for the supercooled condition (1951: 15). Adducts between $BF_3$ and a number of acetates exhibit an enhancement of this effect with increasing length of the alkyl group (1952: 4).

### c) Electrical conductivity

Measurements of electrical conductivity have been used extensively for the study of ionic dissociation in addition compounds (to be treated later) and also for the determination of molecular species in melts or solutions. In general, however, the possibility of achieving one or both of these aims has lacked careful consideration. It seems fair to say that the work of GREENWOOD and MARTIN (1953: 10) has established a new standard. As mentioned above, a number of determinations of activation energies of viscous flow have been made. These and other papers give values for the activation energies of ionic migration (1951: 13, 14; 1953: 3; 1957: 17; 1958: 28; 1959: 31), too.

The important result is that for a given system these two activation energies are of the same order of magnitude, and are in fact very similar. This implies that "similar configurational changes occur in ionic migration and viscous flow". According to GREENWOOD and MARTIN this in turn implies that the reduced conductivity (the product of viscosity coefficient and molar or specific conductivity) is a measure of the degree of ionic self-dissociation, defined as the number of kinetically free ions formed from the adduct molecules. These authors first give careful consideration to the experimental evidence necessary to ensure that the conductivity is due to self-dissociation. The calculation also requires an estimate of the mobility in a standard state, and it is shown that this can be done with a fair degree of accuracy. Values for the degree of dissociation found in this way are of the following order: 5% for $BF_3 \cdot CH_3COOH$, 0.2% for $BF_3 \cdot CH_3COOC_2H_5$, 60–70% for $BF_3 \cdot H_3PO_4$ (see p. 54 concerning this adduct), 0.5% for $GaCl_3 \cdot POCl_3$ and 1% for $GaBr_3 \cdot POBr_3$ (1957:17; 1958: 28).

The similarity between the activation energies suggests the possibility of determining molecular compositions from conductivity measurements, provided that the trend in the degrees of dissociation does not oppose the effect of gradual formation of adduct molecules. It is by no means certain that this is so and it is therefore necessary to discuss in detail the predictions that can be made regarding the shape of the conductivity isotherm if adduct formation takes place.

The electrical conductivity in a binary system is largely determined by two factors. The *activation energy of ionic migration* is determined by any adduct molecules present, which are generally larger and have higher activation energies than the pure components. (If no adducts are formed the activation energy is determined by the interacting molecules.) The electrical conductivity also depends upon the *number of ions present*. The operation of the first factor leads to a lower conductivity than that of the original components. If the adduct molecules are more dissociated than the components, the second factor leads to a higher conductivity.

A very instructive example of the influence of changes in viscosity on electrical conductivity has been given by KLOCHKO (1938: 8). In the system $AlBr_3 \cdot C_6H_5NO_2$ the conductivity isotherm has two maxima (near the eutectic points) and one singular minimum point (at the 1:1 composition). The latter is not displaced by temperature variations but is always located at the same composition. Adduct formation is clearly a prerequisite for ionic dissociation but the increased viscosity due to adduct formation counteracts the effect of an increasing number of ions, and conductivity maxima are obtained near the eutectic points. At the composition of the adduct the number of ions varies little but the viscosity increases sharply (cf. preceding discussions) and a singular minimum point is obtained. Such a curve (the general shape is shown in Fig. 6) must be considered as strong evidence for adduct formation. (The temperature dependence of viscosity and conductivity also indicates compound formation (1938: 8).) A similar shape for the conductivity isotherm has been found in the systems $BF_3$—$CH_3COOH$ (1951: 14), $BF_3$—$CH_3COOC_2H_5$ (1953: 3) and $TiCl_4$—$CH_3COOC_4H_9$ (i) (1952: 14). In some other cases only the initial maximum has been found, but no sharp minimum as in the system $TiCl_4$—$POCl_3$ (1956: 18).

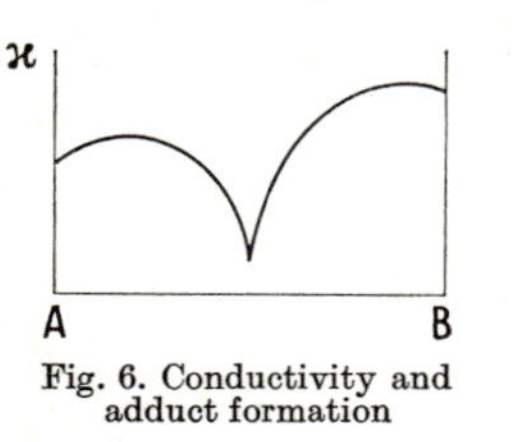

Fig. 6. Conductivity and adduct formation

A sharp minimum point, of the same type as is found in binary systems, was also observed when $AlCl_3$—$C_6H_5COCH_3$ was studied in $SO_2Cl_2$ (1952: 16) (at the 1:1 composition) while other investigations (in nitrobenzene) have led to less understandable results even though they clearly indicate the occurrence of adduct formation (1951: 12, 16; 1954: 17).

The fact that a number of maxima have been found in a system with more than one adduct (1961: 20) demonstrates that the activation energy of ionic migration is determined not only by the molecular volume of the adduct but also by the structure of the liquid. When two adduct molecules are present in similar amounts (as at the eutectic between two adducts) the configurational changes can probably occur more readily because of the relative disorder of the liquid system at this composition compared with that at the composition of the pure adducts.

In the system $BF_3$—$H_3PO_4$ the electrical conductivity *decreases* on the addition of $BF_3$ to $H_3PO_4$ and this exceptional behaviour ($H_3PO_4$ should have an increased acid strength, see p. 47) has been explained in terms of a change from a proton switch conduction mechanism in $H_3PO_4$ to common ionic migration in the binary system (1959: 31). It is suggested that $[H_4PO_4]^+$ and $[H_2PO_2(OBF_3)_2]^-$ are the ions present in the latter case.

A recent discussion of the conductivity of the system $AlCl_3$—$C_6H_5NO_2$ does not consider the influence of viscosity changes (1958: 34).

### d) Ionic dissociation of molecular adducts

**Increased conductivity.** The fact that adduct formation is connected with increased ionic dissociation has been observed in a large number of systems, and in many cases the results reported have been limited to this observation. Examples of increased conductivity are as follows: aldehydes and ketones (1932: 8; 1934: 6, 7; 1941: 2; 1955: 6) (critical observations in 1959: 16), carboxylic acids (1934: 7), acyl chlorides (1932: 8; 1956: 16), nitrobenzene (1934: 8), $POCl_3$ (1952: 11) and $SO_2Cl_2$ (1954: 13).

**Titration studies.** Something must be said about the considerable number of titrations in which some of the donor molecules discussed in this book have been used as solvents. Most of these were conductimetric titrations, but potentiometric and indicator titrations have also been reported. Such titrations do not in themselves yield much direct information about the adducts formed with the solvent; they merely show that the titration reaction can be carried out in the solvent. It is only possible to deduce anything about the donor properties of the solvent and the reactions of the adducts if it can be shown that each reactant is independently capable of producing in the solvent similar changes of conductivity, potential or indicator colour. This point has not always been appreciated in discussions of titration studies.

Consideration will now be given to titration reactions and to a number of other studies, with regard to the extent to which the electrical conductivity is determined by internal ion-molecule exchange in adduct molecules and by other ion transfer reactions. The general nature of halide ion transfer reactions was emphasized by GUTMANN and LINDQVIST (1954: 14) and the use of potentiometric measurements for the study of halide ion activity was recommended (1955: 12, 13). Most of the titration studies have in fact demonstrated the usefulness of these ideas, and all the following titrations can be considered as examples of halide ion transfer titrations.

Conductimetric titrations in: $CH_3COCl$ (1959: 47), $C_6H_5COCl$ (1957: 26), $C_6H_5COBr$ (1959: 26), $(C_2H_5O)_3PO$ (1961: 33), $C_6H_5POCl_2$ (1961: 34), $POCl_3$ (1953: 11; 1956: 19; 1958: 32; 1960: 43), $SOCl_2$ (1952: 15; 1956: 19), $SO_2Cl_2$ (1954: 15), $SO_2$ (1937: 7; 1943: 1; 1944: 2) and $SeOCl_2$ (1956: 19; 1959: 48, 49).

Potentiometric titrations in: $C_6H_5COCl$ (1957: 26, 27), $C_6H_5COBr$ (1959: 26), $C_6H_5POCl_2$ (1961: 35), $POCl_3$ (1957: 28; 1960: 43) and $SOCl_2$ (1955: 6).

Indicator titrations in: $C_6H_5COCl$ (1958: 35; 1959: 50; 1961: 36) and $POCl_3$ (1957: 28). GUTMANN and his collaborators have also developed the use of spectroscopic methods (the identification of the visible spectrum of $FeCl_4^-$) to study ion transfer reactions, and the following solvents have been studied: $(C_4H_9O)_3PO$ (1961: 37), $(C_2H_5O)_3PO$ (1961: 33), $C_6H_5POCl_2$ (1961: 34, 35, 38, 39) and $POCl_3$ (1960: 43, 53; 1961: 40).

The net result of these studies has been to establish a scale of chloride ion donor-acceptor properties for a number of inorganic halides. The order of the compounds is not quite the same in all the solvents, but the general trend is quite consistent. This method has also made it possible to show that $AlCl_3$ (1961: 32) and $TiCl_4$ (1960: 54), which are always found in the middle of the donor as well as the acceptor scale, have amphoteric properties with respect to halide ion transfer. For a negative ion, such as $TiCl_5^-$, one solvent molecule obviously completes the octahedral coordination, while for a positive ion such as $TiCl_3^+$ three solvent molecules are needed. As a result of these reactions the nature of the solvent will influence the extent of the halide ion transfer processes.

This is also found from comparisons of ion transfer processes in $C_6H_5COCl$, $POCl_3$, $C_6H_5POCl_2$ and $(C_4H_9O)_3PO$ (1961: 37, 41, 42). The extent of ion transfer decreases in the order given.

Another result of these studies is that in some cases it seems necessary to introduce the idea that polymeric species are present in the solutions (1959: 34, 53).

In spite of all the research referred to above, there are still few facts available regarding adducts formed between different acceptor molecules and solvent donor molecules, but only about reactions which occur in the donors as solvents. However, at this point the discussion reverts to the increase in ionic dissociation obtained by donor-acceptor reactions, and the various possible interpretations will now be given.

**Possible dissociation reactions.** To simplify the subsequent discussion, $SbCl_5$ will be used as an example of an acceptor halide without any consideration being given to its specific properties.

The simplest explanation for the dissociation of $SbCl_5 \cdot D$ is that the adduct undergoes an internal exchange reaction: $2SbCl_5D = SbCl_4D_2^+ + SbCl_6^-$. Such a reaction is possible with any type of donor molecule and it is consistent with the observed increase in electrical conductivity. It has been claimed that this is the only type of dissociation which need be considered (1961: 33).

For donor molecules containing halogen atoms, however, the occurrence of an alternative reaction has been suggested: $SbCl_5(POCl_3) + nPOCl_3 = SbCl_6^- + POCl_2^+(POCl_3)_n$ (1958: 36). The excess $POCl_3$ is necessary to solvate the $POCl_2^+$ ion.

The following discussion will be confined to experimental evidence for one or other of these suggestions in the case where the donor molecules are potential chloride ion donors (See further discussion on p. 109). There is a considerable body of evidence which appears to support the assumption that the transfer of chloride ions from the donor molecules is an important alternative reaction (1957: 27; 1959: 34; 1960: 43; 1961: 34, 35). Most of this evidence is inconclusive, however, and a typical example is provided by the results of potentiometric studies, which indicate a decrease of the chloride ion activity in $POCl_3$ on addition of $SbCl_5$. At first sight the effect would seem to be possible only in the event of halogen ion transfer, but if the self-dissociation of $POCl_3$ gives rise to fewer chloride ions than is afforded by the solubility of the molybdenum chlorides (present on the molybdenum electrodes) the result only shows that $SbCl_5$ is a stronger chloride ion acceptor than the solvent. In this connection it is not possible to pursue the question sufficiently to be able to say whether there is any definite evidence in these studies for the alternative reaction, but a few comments can be made.

One obvious difference between the two dissociation paths is that the number of osmotically active ions produced by the addition of one

$SbCl_5$ acceptor molecule is *one* in the general case, ($2SbCl_5 + POCl_3 = SbCl_4(POCl_3)_2^+ + SbCl_6^-$) but *two* in the alternative reaction ($SbCl_5 + POCl_3 = SbCl_6^- + POCl_2^+$). The conductivity measurements in dilute solutions, referred to above, indicate that in fact more than one ion is formed, and that this reaction is therefore favoured in very dilute solutions of the acceptor molecule in a donor solvent. The same conclusion is reached from cryoscopic studies in $SOCl_2$, which indicate that more than one osmotically active particle is formed in dilute solutions (1955: 6).

The results of some exchange reactions might also be considered to support the conclusions based on the conductometric, potentiometric and spectrophotometric studies. In general the exchange rate for $Cl^{36}$ between acceptor and donor molecules is very slow, as is shown by experiments with $SbCl_5$ and $AlCl_3$ in $POCl_3$ (1957: 29) and $FeCl_3$ in $SeOCl_2$ (1956: 30). In a study of the system $BCl_3$—$POCl_3$ Herber (1960: 64) obtained the same result, but also observed that, although the rate is very low in an excess of $BCl_3$, it increases with an excess of $POCl_3$. The general dissociation reaction $2BCl_3 \cdot POCl_3 = BCl_2(POCl_3)_2^+ + BCl_4^-$ would not lead to chlorine exchange at any concentration of $BCl_3$ while the alternative reaction $BCl_3POCl_3 + nPOCl_3 = BCl_4^- + POCl_2^+(POCl_3)_n$ would favour chlorine exchange in an excess of $POCl_3$. Accordingly, exchange experiments seem to support the view that halogen ion exchange is of some importance in dilute solutions of the donor.

To sum up the available evidence, it seems most probable that the general dissociation reaction is the most important one, but that the alternative reaction cannot be ignored even if in the past it has been overestimated to some extent. All kinds of intermediate cases are also possible, and further studies are necessary if a definite answer is to be found to this intriguing but rather special problem.

**Electrolysis and transport numbers.** Experiments of this type have not given results which permit many definite conclusions to be drawn regarding the nature either of adduct molecules in solution, or of the ions formed by the dissociation reactions. The principal reason is that in general the basic physical chemistry behind these studies has been less firmly established than is customary for similar studies in aqueous solution.

Gutmann and his collaborators have made attempts to determine transport numbers for solutions of $SbCl_5$ and $AlCl_3$ in $POCl_3$ (1955: 14). The transport of Sb and Al (to the anode) is very small compared with the transport of P (to the cathode) and some kind of switch mechanism for the conductivity therefore seems probable. This would also be possible in dilute solutions in which, according to the conclusions of the preceding section, some solvated $POCl_2^+$ ions should be present. The occurrence of the following electrode processes is suggested: $SbCl_6^- = SbCl_5 + \frac{1}{2}Cl_2 + e^-$ and $POCl_2^+ + e^- = \frac{1}{2}POCl + \frac{1}{2}POCl_3$. The compostition of amorphous, black POCl is not firmly established.

Similar studies of $AlCl_3$ in acyl halides indicate that Al is transported to both electrodes, but that slightly more travels to the anode (1932: 8). Many studies of $SnCl_4$ and other acceptors in esters and carboxylic acids have also been reported (1953: 12; 1954: 16; 1957: 30; 1958: 37, 38; 1959: 46, 51, 52). The results quoted show some divergence and seem to contribute little to an understanding of these solutions. It is possible, however, that the position will be clarified by the ideas developed in a recent paper which, at the moment of writing, is not available for detailed study (1959: 51).

**Other studies.** An interesting observation is that the conductivity seems to be higher for associated adducts than for the monomers (1955 :9).

Recently Baaz and Gutmann have also attempted and partly succeeded in applying the theories for dilute salt solutions in water to other solvents, mainly $POCl_3$. These studies do not fall directly within the scope of this book, but in connection with the discussions of ionic dissociation they might be of some interest to the reader who wishes to pursue the subject further (1959: 54; 1960: 55).

## 21. Affinity studies

This heading covers discussions of free energy and enthalpy changes in donor-acceptor reactions. Unfortunately most of the studies reported do not give direct information about donor-acceptor interaction since the systems studied have generally included condensed phases. The ideal reaction to study would be $D(g) + A(g) = DA(g)$. In general, however, the adducts are not sufficiently volatile to permit such studies, and the closest approach that can be made to ideal conditions is provided by studies in solution, using solvents which interact very little with either the components or the adduct. In order to obtain direct information regarding the donor-acceptor interaction in instances where liquid or solid components or adducts take part in the reaction, a knowledge of cohesion energies becomes necessary. This condition is not fulfilled in most of the studies carried out so far, and in such cases the detailed results have not been presented but only the relative values which seem to be of interest. The free energy changes cannot be correlated directly with a chemical bond model in the same way as the enthalpy changes (strictly only at absolute zero) but in most of the cases studied, both thermodynamical functions give affinity orders which are similar.

The studies of free energy changes will be classified as equilibrium studies, and those of enthalpy changes as thermochemical studies.

### a) Equilibrium studies

The most direct approach to affinity problems is the study of displacement reactions. If in the reaction $AD_{(1)} + D_{(2)} = AD_{(2)} + D_{(1)}$ the donor molecule $D_{(2)}$ can replace the donor molecule $D_{(1)}$, the free energy of formation of $AD_{(2)}$ from the components is lower than that of $AD_{(1)}$. (The free energy of formation is a negative quantitity.)

An early and very extensive study of displacement reactions relating to donor-acceptor reactions was made by Mensutkin (1909: 5). He did not study molecular adducts but the reactions $MgX_2 \cdot 6D_{(1)}(s) + 6D_{(2)}(l)$

$=MgX_2 \cdot 6D_{(2)}(s) + 6D_{(1)}(l)$, and the interpretation is therefore more complicated. This reaction corresponds to a displacement of $D_{(1)}$ by $D_{(2)}$. (In a few cases mole ratios other than 1:6 were obtained.) By systematic studies, using $MgCl_2$, $MgBr_2$ and $MgI_2$ as acceptors, MENSUTKIN was able to derive an order for increasing donor strength which is of interest in the present discussion. He found that the donor strength increases on passing from ethers to ketones, aldehydes and esters and further to carboxylic acids and amides, urea heading this sequence with a donor strength greater even than that of water. It is natural that the interpretations offered are not wholly acceptable to-day, but the systematic interest in affinity relations which underlies this study must be acknowledged by modern chemists. Without doubt the greatest difficulty involved in the application of these results is constituted by the lattice energies of the solid adducts, even though it is probable that $MgX_2 \cdot 6D$ adducts have very similar structures independent of the nature of D.

An effort to reduce these difficulties was made in a study of the reaction $SbCl_5 \cdot POCl_3 + (CH_3)_3PO = SbCl_5 \cdot (CH_3)_3PO + POCl_3$, carried out in a dilute solution of ethylene chloride. In this instance Raman spectra were used to demonstrate that the reaction takes place almost quantitatively (1959: 55).

The use of cryoscopic measurements to study equilibria in different solvents has already been mentioned, and some examples will be presented below.

Comparisons between different acceptors with a common donor have been made using this method. Thus using esters, $SnBr_4$ is a weaker acceptor than $SnCl_4$ in $C_2H_4Br_2$ (1924: 4) and $ZrI_4 < ZrBr_4 < ZrCl_4$ in $C_6H_6$ (1959: 20, 41, 42), and using $POCl_3$, $TiCl_4 < ZrCl_4 < HfCl_4$ in $C_6H_5NO_2$ (1960: 50). Extensive comparisons have also been made between different donors with the same acceptor, namely $SnCl_4$ in $C_2H_4Br_2$ or $C_6H_6$ (1924: 4). The following interesting sequences have been found: $C_6H_5CHO > C_6H_5CH = CHCOOC_2H_5 > C_6H_5CH_2CH_2COC_2H_5 > C_6H_5COOC_2H_5$ and $CH_2(COOC_2H_5)_2 > (COOC_2H_5)_2 > (CH_2COOC_2H_5)_2 > (CHCOOC_2H_5)_2$. In another study it has been shown that using $AlBr_3$ as the acceptor, $CH_3NO_2$ is a stronger donor than $C_6H_5NO_2$ (1959: 56).

Equilibria have also been studied using other methods. Heats of reaction have been used to derive the relative acceptor strengths of the following compounds in $C_6H_5Cl$ using $C_6H_5CHO$: $AlCl_3 > FeCl_3 > SbCl_3$ (1949: 7). Another interesting method is the determination of equilibria by spectrophotometry. Thus the displacement reaction $BF_3 \cdot (C_2H_5)_2O$ (in ether) $+ D = BF_3 \cdot D + (C_2H_5)_2O$ has been studied with donors which give UV spectra suitable for the application of this technique. The following order of donor strengths has been found: $CH_3COC_6H_4OCH_3(p) > CH_3COC_6H_4CH_3(p) > CH_3COC_6H_5$ (1961: 43).

In this connection a direct determination of the free energy change $\Delta F$ should also be mentioned. This has been made for the reaction $BCl_3$ (g, 1 atm) $+ POCl_3$ (g, 1 atm) $= BCl_3 \cdot POCl_3$ (s). At $25^0$ a value $\Delta F = -4{\cdot}6$ kcal/mole has been found. The value is based on measurements of dissociation pressures (1943: 4).

Finally the thermal stabilities of similar adducts give some idea about the strength of the donor-acceptor interaction. For instance, consideration of these properties has led to the conclusion that using $CH_3COOC_2H_5$ as the donor the order of acceptor strength is $ZrCl_4 > ZrCl_3(OC_2H_5) >$ $> ZrCl_2(OC_2H_5)_2 > ZrCl(OC_2H_5)_3$ (1950: 5).

## b) Thermochemical studies

In each of a considerable number of calorimetric studies which have been made, at least one condensed phase has been included, and the results cannot therefore be used for direct discussions of donor-acceptor interaction. In the following survey not all the available $\Delta H$ values will be presented, but reference will be made to the systems studied. Where a valid comparison seems reasonable, however, the order of relative donor or acceptor strengths are given even if a condensed phase is present.

The different acceptors are treated in the same systematic order as before.

**$MgI(OC_2H_5)$.** The general reaction $MgI(OC_2H_5)$ (in $C_6H_6$) + Donor (in $C_6H_6$) = Adduct (s) has been studied (1924: 7) for a number of ketones and esters. These all give enthalpy changes of the same order of magnitude (10–18 kcal/mole) and the differences between some of the members of the series given below are so small that the lattice energies might be of decisive importance. For ketones the observed order is: $(CH_3)_2CO > CH_3COC_6H_5 > CH_3COC_2H_5 > (C_6H_5)_2CO > CH_3COC_6H_{13}$. The corresponding order for esters is $HCOOC_2H_5 \gg C_2H_5COOC_2H_5 >$ $> CH_3COOC_2H_5 > C_6H_5COOC_2H_5 > C_6H_5COOC_6H_5$. These values are all much higher than for ethyl ether (5 kcal/mole) and it is interesting to note that some pyrones give enthalpy changes of the order of 11 kcal/mole, indicating that the oxygen atom of the $C=O$ bond is the donor atom (see p. 12). On the other hand all ketones and esters give much lower heats of reaction than do amines (1925: 10). Studies of this type are relevant to Grignard reactions and it has been shown that excessively strong donors can prevent the formation of adducts with ketones, a step which is a prerequisite for reduction (1952: 2).

**$BF_3$, $BCl_3$, and $BBr_3$.** The reactions $BX_3(l) + C_6H_5NO_2(l) = BX_3 \cdot$ $\cdot C_6H_5NO_2$ (solution in $C_6H_5NO_2$) have been studied (1956: 17). The order $BF_3 < BCl_3 < BBr_3$ has been clearly established. The heats of reaction are in the range 6–13 kcal/mole. The corresponding value for $CH_3COCl$ in excess $CH_3COCl$ with $BCl_3$ as the acceptor is much smaller, of the order of 1 kcal/mole (1960: 38).

**$AlCl_3$, $AlBr_3$ and $AlI_3$.** The reaction $AlX_3(s) + D(l) +$ excess $C_6H_5Cl$ $= AlX_3 \cdot D$ (sol. in $C_6H_5Cl$) has been studied (1949: 7; 1950: 6) but in most cases some precipitation of the adduct has also occurred. With $C_6H_5CHO$ the order $AlCl_3 < AlBr < AlI_3$ seems to be firmly established, however, and with $AlCl_3$ as acceptor the order of donor strengths is $C_6H_5CHO >$ $> CH_3COC_6H_5 > (C_6H_5)_2CO$. It is also clear that the heats of reaction for these compounds (15–25 kcal/mole) are much higher than for $C_6H_5NO_2$ or $CH_3OC_6H_5$ (8 kcal/mole) but smaller than for pyridine (48 kcal/mole).

An earlier study does not agree completely with these results (1941: 3).

A painstaking attempt has been made to determine $\Delta H$ for the reaction $AlBr_3(g) + D(g) = AlBr_3 \cdot D(g)$ by considering all the solvation and crystallization energies for the reaction taking place in $C_2H_4Br_2$ (1951: 17). Values in kcal/mole for $-\Delta H$ using different D molecules are 20.4 with $CH_3COC_6H_5$, 19.9 with $(C_6H_5)_2CO$, 14.3 with $C_6H_5COBr$ and 9.1 with $C_3H_7COBr$.

**$GaCl_3$.** One ideal reaction has been studied, namely $GaCl_3(g) + POCl_3(g) = GaCl_3 \cdot POCl_3(g)$. The value of $-\Delta H$ is 22.6 kcal/mole (1957: 18).

Reactions of the type $GaCl_3(s) + D(l) = GaCl_3 \cdot D(s)$ have also been compared. The order found is $(CH_3)_2CO > POCl_3 > CH_3COCl$ (1957: 18; 1958: 20; 1960: 38). The heat of reaction with pyridine is much larger, while ether gives values of the same order of magnitude as acetone (1958: 20).

**$SnCl_4$.** An extensive study has been made of the reaction $SnCl_4(g) + 2D(g) = SnCl_4 \cdot 2D(s)$. Here D stands for a monofunctional donor (monoesters) or half a bifunctional donor (diesters) (1940: 5). The order found is $C_6H_5COOC_2H_5 > C_2H_5COOC_2H_5 > C_5H_{10}(COOC_2H_5)_2 > C_4H_8(COOC_2H_5)_2 > C_3H_6(COOC_2H_5)_2 > CH_2(COOC_2H_5)_2 > C_2H_4(COOC_2H_5)_2 > (COOC_2H_5)_2$. (Observe the differences from the corresponding equilibria studies (p. 59)). Amines give higher heats of reaction.

These results, as far as they permit valid comparisons, can be related to those for other donors by the qualitative studies of reactions $SnCl_4 + 2D = SnCl_4 \cdot 2D$ in $C_2H_4Cl_2$ (1960: 56, 57; 1961: 44, 45). The order obtained as a result of these studies (and from some unpublished results) is: $(C_6H_5)_2SeO = (C_6H_5)_3AsO > (CH_3)_3PO > (C_6H_5)_3PO > (C_4H_9O)_3PO = (CH_3O)_2SeO > (CH_3O)_3PO > (C_6H_5O)_3PO > (CH_3)_2CO = CH_3COOC_2H_5 > (C_2H_5)_2CO > (CH_3)_2SO_2 > (CH_3O)_2SO > POCl_3 = (CH_3)(CH_3O)SO_2$. Some other types of donors have been compared and it has been found that amines are stronger donors than all oxo-compounds and that ethers are of the same strength as ketones. It has also been shown that amides are much better donors than ketones and esters. Finally thioamides are similar to amides and $PSCl_3$ is much weaker than $POCl_3$.

Similar measurements of heats of reaction between the pure components have been reported in some cases (1938: 9). The interaction with $C_6H_5CHO$ has also been investigated (1949: 7).

**$TiCl_4$.** The reaction $TiCl_4(l) + D(l) = TiCl_4 \cdot D(l)$ (supercooled) has been studied with different esters (1955: 11, 15; 1960: 58). The observed order is: $CH_3COOC_2H_5 > CH_3COOC_3H_7 > CH_3COOC_4H_9 > CH_3COOC_5H_{11} > HCOOC_4H_9 = HCOOC_5H_{11}$.

The authors have tried to calculate values for the corresponding 1:2 adducts and claim that their results are in agreement with their earlier interpretations of viscosity and conductivity studies (1954: 18).

The reactions with $C_6H_5CHO$ (1949: 7) and $POCl_3$ (1956: 18) have also been studied.

**$ZrCl_4$, $ZrBr_4$ and $HfCl_4$.** The types of reaction studied are $ZrCl_4(s) + 1$ or $2D(l) = ZrCl_4 \cdot D(s)$ or $ZrCl_4 \cdot 2D(s)$ (1952: 8; 1954: 8; 1960: 59). The most remarkable result is that the extra energy gained from the addition of the second donor molecule is very small compared with that from the first step (of the order of 4 kcal/mole). This is a strong indication that the 1:1 adduct is polymeric. The difference between $ZrCl_4$ and $ZrBr_4$ is also very small. For the 1:2 adducts the heat of reaction with benzoate is slightly larger than for the esters of the aliphatic carboxylic acids. The differences are rather small, however. The heat of reaction with one mole of esters of phthalic acid, on the other hand, is significantly lower than for two moles of the monoesters. The same has been found for $HfCl_4$. The interaction with $C_6H_5CHO$ has also been studied (1949: 7).

**$SbCl_5$ and $SbCl_3$.** The reactions $SbCl_5(sol.) + D(sol.) = SbCl_5 \cdot D(sol.)$ have been studied in ethylene chloride using a wide variety of donors (1960: 56, 57; 1961: 44, 45 and unpublished results). These qualitative investigations indicate the order for the heats of these reactions. It can safely be assumed that the variations in solvation energies are very small (see below) and the same order can therefore be expected for the gas phase reactions. The sequence is as follows: $(C_6H_5)_2SeO = (C_6H_5)_3AsO >$ $> (CH_3)_3PO > (CH_3)_2SO > (C_4H_9O)_3PO > (CH_3O)_3PO = (CH_3O)_2SeO >$ $> (C_6H_5O)_3PO > (CH_3)_2CO = CH_3COOC_2H_5 = (C_2H_5)_2CO > (CH_3O)_2SO =$ $= (CH_3)_2SO_2 > (C_6H_5)_2SO_2 = POCl_3 > (CH_3)(CH_3O)SO_2 > SOCl_2$. Ethers give heats of reaction of the same order of magnitude as esters, while amides give much higher values. $PSCl_3$ gives a much lower value than $POCl_3$, and thioamides almost the same as amides.

The main difference compared with the order found using $SnCl_4$ is that sulfones and sulfonates are comparatively stronger donors with $SnCl_4$ than with $SbCl_5$.

Quantitative calorimetric studies (1962: 20) have since shown that the solvation energies of a number of donors do not vary more than from 0.1 to 0.4 kcal/mole. The values of the heats of reaction found with some donors are:

| | | | |
|---|---|---|---|
| $(CH_3)_2CO$ | 17.04 kcal/mole | $C_3H_7COOC_2H_5$ | 16.77 kcal/mole |
| $CH_3COOCH_3$ | 16.40 kcal/mole | $(CH_3O)_2CO$ | 15.18 kcal/mole |
| $CH_3COOC_2H_5$ | 17.10 kcal/mole | $(C_2H_5O)_2CO$ | 16.00 kcal/mole |
| $CH_3COOC_3H_7(i)$ | 17.54 kcal/mole | | |

The much higher heats of reaction found with amides in the qualitative studies have also been confirmed by more accurate investigations, the observed values being 28.62 kcal/mole for $CH_3CON(CH_3)_2$ and 30.53 kcal/mole for $CO[N(CH_3)_2]_2$ (1962: 20). In these cases the heats of solvation are 0.9–1.1 kcal/mole for the donor molecules.

The same type of reaction has also been studied using $SbCl_3$ as the acceptor molecule (1960: 56 and unpublished results). Here the compositions of the adducts are less certain and are different. Only results for the 1:1 compositions have been compared and the order found is very similar even if the sulfones and sulfonates are comparatively stronger donors with $SbCl_3$ than with $SbCl_5$: $(CH_3)_2SO > (C_4H_9O)_3PO = (CH_3O)_3PO >$ $> (C_6H_5O)_3PO = (CH_3)_2CO = (CH_3)_2SO_2 > CH_3COOC_2H_5 > (CH_3O)_2SO =$ $= POCl_3 = (CH_3)(CH_3O)SO_2 = CH_3COOH$. Since all the heats of reaction are rather low this sequence is less certain than those obtained using $SnCl_4$ and $SbCl_5$.

Some direct comparisons between $SbCl_5$ and $SbCl_3$ have also been made with the same donor molecule $(CH_3)_3PO$ in 1:1 mole ratio (1960: 23) and some less comparable reactions with $C_6H_5CHO$ have also been studied (1949: 7). In both cases the results clearly indicate that $SbCl_5$ is a much stronger acceptor than $SbCl_3$.

At this point, it may be mentioned that the order of hydrogen bond strength for different acid solvents with $(C_4H_9O)_3PO$, $(C_2H_5O)_3PO$ and $POCl_3$ indicates the same order of donor strength for these compounds as that found using $SbCl_5$ as the acceptor molecule (1955: 16).

**$FeCl_3$.** The interaction with $C_6H_5CHO$ has been studied (1949: 7).

**$CoCl_2$.** The interaction with acetone has been studied (1956: 14).

Using a few auxiliary assumptions, DILKE and ELEY (1949: 7) have calculated the heats of formation for each donor-acceptor bond formed between $C_6H_5CHO$, dissolved in $C_6H_5Cl$, and different acceptor molecules. The values are not firmly established but they give some idea regarding the order of acceptor strengths. After making a correction for solvation, the heats of reaction have been divided by the number of donor-acceptor bonds. The values in kcal/mole are $AlI_3$ 54, $AlBr_3$ 49, $AlCl_3$ 39, $FeCl_3$ 27, $SbCl_5$ 21, $TiCl_4$ 17, $SnCl_4$ 14, $ZrCl_4$ 9, $SbCl_3$ 4. Similar but more accurate studies would be of great interest.

## 22. Structural data

This section deals mainly with bond lengths and bond angles as determined by X-ray crystallography, but also includes some spectroscopic results. Unfortunately not enough accurate work has been done in this field, which obviously offers many interesting problems of structural chemistry.

The different donor types have been treated in the same order as in the systematic section.

All accurate structure determinations are presented together with figures and tables listing all the bond lengths and bond angles within the molecules. Interested readers are referred to the original papers for information about contact distances and other details, which are of little interest in the present context.

**Donor molecules containing the $>C{=}O$ group.** It is disconcerting to find that no accurate structure determinations have been reported for adducts with aldehydes, ketones or quinones. The weakening of the $C = O$ bond has been established by spectroscopic methods and, as mentioned earlier, has been used to show which oxygen atom is the donor in carboxylic acids, esters and lactones.

An attempt has been made to systematize the spectroscopic results found for adducts of ketones with different acceptor compounds (1958: 6; 1959: 57). With acetophenone as the donor the following order of increased negative shift in $cm^{-1}$ was observed for solid 1:1 adducts: $HgCl_2$ 18, $ZnCl_2$ 47, $BF_3$ 107, $TiCl_4$ 118, $AlCl_3$ 120, $FeCl_3$ 130, $AlBr_3$ 130 and with benzophenone as donor: $BF_3$ 112, $AlCl_3$ 122, $AlBr_3$ 142, $TiCl_4$ 144 and $FeCl_3$ 145. The order has thus been partly reversed but in all cases the adducts with the purely aromatic ketones show the highest negative shifts. Of these acceptors reacting with acetone, only $BF_3$ and $AlBr_3$ have been studied and the negative shifts are still lower than in the acetophenone adducts (70 and 85 $cm^{-1}$). Some other acceptors which react with acetone have been investigated and the shifts found are 22 $cm^{-1}$ ($AsCl_3$), 30 $cm^{-1}$ ($SbCl_3$) (1960: 23) and 75 $cm^{-1}$ ($SnCl_4$) (1958: 4). The first two values are for 1:1 compositions in the liquid state and the third for a solid 1:2 adduct (the composition 1:1 in the original paper is probably a misprint) so that the values are not directly comparable.

It has also been observed that there is an increase in the antisymmetrical C—C chain vibration frequency of acetone in adducts with $CdCl_2$, $HgCl_2$, $HgBr_2$ (1959:5), $BF_3$ (1958:7), $AlBr_3$ (1958:4) and $SbCl_3$ (1960:23).

The crystal structure of $HgCl_2\cdot$ O =O has been determined but has not been refined by modern methods (1953: 1), and only the most striking features of the structure will be mentioned. The geometry of the linear $HgCl_2$ molecule is unchanged and the Hg—Cl bond length is 2.33 Å. The donor oxygen atom of the C=O bond is added perpendicular to the linear $HgCl_2$ molecule and the Hg—O distance is 2.38 Å. Three chlorine atoms in neighbouring $HgCl_2$ molecules complete the distorted octahedron around the mercury atom, and interact very weakly with it at distances of 2.94, 3.18 and 3.34 Å. The C=O bond length in the adduct is 1.32 Å and the lactone C—O bond length 1.38 Å. Even if the accuracy is not very high this indicates that the C=O bond is weakened and the lactone bond strengthened by the adduct formation.

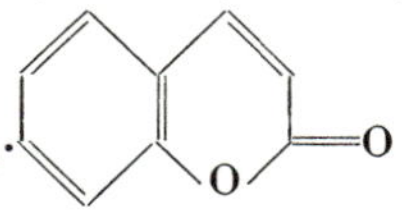

The infrared studies of adducts with carboxylic acids and esters have confirmed the weakening of the C=O bond (p. 12) and have also given evidence of a positive shift of what is now recognized as an antisymmetrical C—C—O vibration frequency (1960: 24; 1961: 7, 9; 1962: 19). Compare the effect on the C—C—C vibration in ketones (see above).

It has been assumed that the hydrogen bond polymerization of carboxylic acids remains unbroken by adduct formation with acceptor molecules such as $SnCl_4$ and $SbCl_3$ (1961: 9). This has been confirmed cryoscopically by the determination of the dimerization of $SnCl_4\cdot 2RCOOH$ adducts (1961: 46). On the other hand, the hydrogen bond system is almost completely destroyed by the stronger acceptor molecule of $SbCl_5$ (1961: 9).

Infrared studies give indication of a similar disruption of the internal hydrogen bonding in salicylic aldehyde on adduct formation with $HgCl_2$ (1962: 27).

The fact that the negative shift of the C=O vibration frequency is larger in $BF_3$ adducts with $CH_3COOC_2H_5$ (—119 $cm^{-1}$) than with $(CH_3)_2CO$ (—70 $cm^{-1}$) has been considered as evidence for stronger interaction in the former case (1961: 7).

The donor strengths of ketones and esters have also been compared on the basis of their weakening of the Hg—Cl bonds in $HgCl_2$ adducts. The negative shifts found are: 21 $cm^{-1}$ with $CH_3COOC_2H_5$, 24 $cm^{-1}$ with $HCOOCH_3$ and 24 $cm^{-1}$ with $(CH_3)_2CO$ (1958:39).

It has also been suggested recently that the negative shift of the C=O vibration frequency in $CH_3COOC_2H_5$ can be considered as a measure of the acceptor strengths of different acceptor molecules (1962: 25). This is possible only if very similar adducts are compared. The results indicate the sequence $AlBr_3 > AlCl_3$ but $InCl_3 > InBr_3$, $SnCl_4 > SnBr_4$, $TiCl_4 > TiBr_4$ and $ZrCl_4 > ZrBr_4$. They also show that $BX_3 > GaX_3 > AlX_3 > InX_3$ and $SnX_4 > GeX_4 > SiX_4$ and $TiX_4 > ZrX_4$.

The crystal structure determinations of $CdCl_2$ adducts with a number of amides (Cavalca, Nardelli and collaborators) prove the occurence of addition to the oxygen atom but they also show that these adducts are not molecules but contain infinite chlorine bridges. A very recent structure determination of $SbCl_5 \cdot HCON(CH_3)_2$ (1962: 11) has not been refined sufficiently to permit safe discussion of bond lengths and bond angles.

From spectroscopic studies of amide adducts a few conclusions may be drawn with some certainty even if the evidence is far from conclusive. The main conclusions are that the C=O bond is weakened and the C—N bond strengthened, both effects being larger for $TiCl_4$ than for $TiBr_4$, and the weakening of the C=O bond is smaller than in corresponding ketone adducts. No difference is found between the effects of $BCl_3$ and $BBr_3$ (1958: 11; 1960: 26, 27).

The hydrogen bonds of the amides are broken by the adduct formation with $BCl_3$ and $BBr_3$. The N—H stretching frequencies are shifted, however, towards lower values compared with in the monomeric donor molecules in the gaseous state. It has rightly been pointed out that this does not prove the occurrence of addition to the nitrogen atom (1960:26).

**Donor molecules containing the $\rangle$P=O group.** Systematically, this class of adduct has been most studied from a structural point of view. The three very similar structures of $SbCl_5 \cdot POCl_3$, $SbCl_5 \cdot (CH_3)_3PO$ and $NbCl_5 \cdot POCl_3$ are presented together and bond lengths and bond angles

Table 1. $SbCl_5 \cdot POCl_3$

Bond lengths:

| | | | |
|---|---|---|---|
| Sb(1)—Cl(2) | 2.35 Å | Sb(1)—O(6) | 2.17 Å |
| Sb(1)—Cl(3) | 2.33 Å | P(7)—O(6) | 1.47 Å |
| Sb(1)—Cl(4) | 2.32 Å | P(7)—Cl(8) | 1.95 Å |
| Sb(1)—Cl(5) | 2.33 Å | P(7)—Cl(9) | 1.95 Å |

Bond angles:

| | | | |
|---|---|---|---|
| Cl(2)—Sb(1)—Cl(4) | 93.0° | Cl(5)—Sb(1)—O(6) | 84.9° |
| Cl(2)—Sb(1)—Cl(5) | 89.3° | Sb(1)—O(6)—P(7) | 145.0° |
| Cl(2)—Sb(1)—O(6) | 86.2° | O(6)—P(7)—Cl(8) | 110.9° |
| Cl(3)—Sb(1)—Cl(4) | 95.7° | O(6)—P(7)—Cl(9) | 112.5° |
| Cl(3)—Sb(1)—Cl(5) | 89.9° | Cl(8)—P(7)—Cl(9) | 107.4° |
| Cl(3)—Sb(1)—O(6) | 85.1° | Cl(9)—P(7)—Cl(9) | 105.9° |
| Cl(4)—Sb(1)—Cl(5) | 95.1° | | |

Table 2. $NbCl_5 \cdot POCl_3$

Bond lengths:

| | | | |
|---|---|---|---|
| Nb(1)—Cl(2) | 2.35 Å | Nb(1)—O(6) | 2.16 Å |
| Nb(1)—Cl(3) | 2.29 Å | P(7)—O(6) | 1.45 Å |
| Nb(1)—Cl(4) | 2.25 Å | P(7)—Cl(8) | 1.95 Å |
| Nb(1)—Cl(5) | 2.30 Å | P(7)—Cl(9) | 1.94 Å |

Bond angles:

| | | | |
|---|---|---|---|
| Cl(2)—Nb(1)—Cl(4) | 91.9° | Cl(5)—Nb(1)—O(6) | 83.7° |
| Cl(2)—Nb(1)—Cl(5) | 88.8° | Nb(1)—O(6)—P(7) | 148.8° |
| Cl(2)—Nb(1)—O(6) | 84.6° | O(6)—P(7)—Cl(8) | 111.8° |
| Cl(3)—Nb(1)—Cl(4) | 97.2° | O(6)—P(7)—Cl(9) | 112.2° |
| Cl(3)—Nb(1)—Cl(5) | 90.2° | Cl(8)—P(7)—Cl(9) | 107.1° |
| Cl(3)—Nb(1)—O(6) | 86.3° | Cl(9)—P(7)—Cl(9) | 106.1° |
| Cl(4)—Nb(1)—Cl(5) | 96.2° | | |

Table 3. $SbCl_5 \cdot (CH_3)_3PO$

Bond lengths:

| | | | |
|---|---|---|---|
| Sb(1)—Cl(2) | 2.34 Å | Sb(1)—O(6) | 1.94 Å |
| Sb(1)—Cl(3) | 2.35 Å | P(7)—O(6) | 1.56 Å |
| Sb(1)—Cl(4) | 2.34 Å | P(7)—C(8) | 1.84 Å |
| Sb(1)—Cl(5) | 2.33 Å | P(7)—C(9) | 1.80 Å |

Bond angles:

| | | | |
|---|---|---|---|
| Cl(2)—Sb(1)—Cl(4) | 90.1° | Cl(5)—Sb(1)—O(6) | 87.2° |
| Cl(2)—Sb(1)—Cl(5) | 89.7° | Sb(1)—O(6)—P(7) | 144.9° |
| Cl(2)—Sb(1)—O(6) | 90.7° | O(6)—P(7)—C(8) | 108.1° |
| Cl(3)—Sb(1)—Cl(4) | 91.3° | O(6)—P(7)—C(9) | 109.9° |
| Cl(3)—Sb(1)—Cl(5) | 90.2° | C(8)—P(7)—C(9) | 111.0° |
| Cl(3)—Sb(1)—O(6) | 87.9° | C(9)—P(7)—C(9) | 106.9° |
| Cl(4)—Sb(1)—Cl(5) | 92.8° | | |

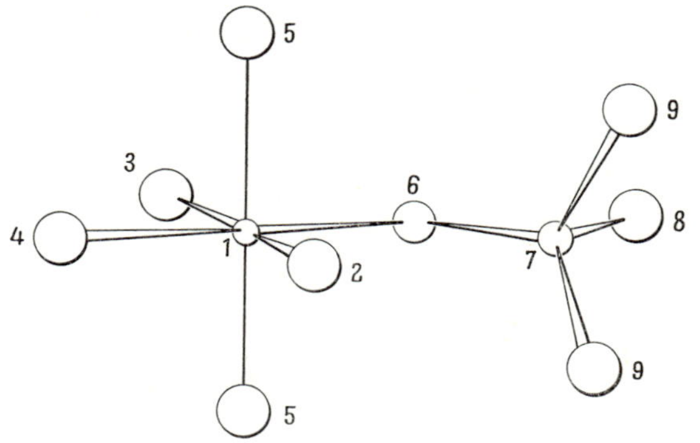

Fig. 7. The structures of $SbCl_5 \cdot POCl_3$, $NbCl_5 \cdot POCl_3$ and $SbCl_5 \cdot (CH_3)_3PO$. Generalized figure

based on refined structure determinations are given (1962: 13). The values for the first two adducts differ only slightly from those presented earlier. Data for $SnCl_4 \cdot 2POCl_3$ (1962: 7) and $(TiCl_4 \cdot POCl_3)_2$ (1960: 1) are also given.

Reference should be made to Figure 7 for the description of the three structures $SbCl_5 \cdot POCl_3$, $NbCl_5 \cdot POCl_3$ and $SbCl_5 \cdot (CH_3)_3PO$ and the appropriate symbols should be applied when the three tables 1–3 of bond lengths and bond angles are read.

The values for $SnCl_4 \cdot 2POCl_3$ in Table 4 refer to Figure 8.

Table 4. $SnCl_4 \cdot 2POCl_3$

Bond lengths:

| | | | |
|---|---|---|---|
| Sn(1)—Cl(2) | 2.31 Å | P(8)—O(6) | 1.49 Å |
| Sn(1)—Cl(3) | 2.36 Å | P(7)—Cl(9) | 1.93 Å |
| Sn(1)—Cl(4) | 2.33 Å | P(7)—Cl(10) | 1.95 Å |
| Sn(1)—O(5) | 2.30 Å | P(8)—Cl(11) | 2.00 Å |
| Sn(1)—O(6) | 2.25 Å | P(8)—Cl(12) | 1.89 Å |
| P(7)—O(5) | 1.41 Å | | |

Bond angles:

| | | | |
|---|---|---|---|
| Cl(2)—Sn(1)—Cl(3) | 103.0° | Sn(1)—O(6)—P(8) | 150.7° |
| Cl(2)—Sn(1)—Cl(4) | 95.5° | O(5)—P(7)—Cl(9) | 110.0° |
| Cl(2)—Sn(1)—O(5) | 89.3° | O(5)—P(7)—Cl(10) | 114.7° |
| Cl(3)—Sn(1)—Cl(4) | 95.7° | Cl(9)—P(7)—Cl(10) | 105.4° |
| Cl(3)—Sn(1)—O(6) | 89.4° | Cl(10)—P(7)—Cl(10) | 105.7° |
| Cl(4)—Sn(1)—O(5) | 82.9° | O(6)—P(8)—Cl(11) | 110.6° |
| Cl(4)—Sn(1)—O(6) | 83.1° | O(6)—P(8)—Cl(12) | 114.7° |
| O(5)—Sn(1)—O(6) | 78.3° | Cl(11)—P(8)—Cl(12) | 101.2° |
| Sn(1)—O(5)—P(7) | 144.5° | Cl(12)—P(8)—Cl(12) | 112.5° |

The accuracy of this structure determination is rather low.

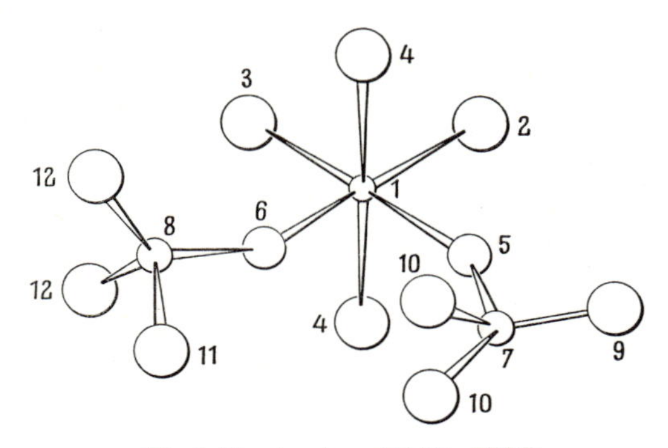


Fig. 8. The structure of $SnCl_4 \cdot 2POCl_3$

The values for $(TiCl_4 \cdot POCl_3)_2$ in Table 5 refer to the bond lengths and bond angles given in Fig. 9.

Negative shifts of the P = O vibration frequency with different donor molecules and different acceptor molecules have been reported in many instances. It has been pointed out (1959: 12; 1960: 15) that comparisons can only be made between adducts with similar structures. In many cases the fulfillment of this condition is either established or is fairly probable, but the comparative studies have not proved very fruitful.

Table 5. $(TiCl_4 \cdot POCl_3)_2$

Bond lengths:

| | | | |
|---|---|---|---|
| Ti(1)—Cl(2) | 2.44 Å | Ti(1)—O(7) | 2.10 Å |
| Ti(1)—Cl(3) | 2.54 Å | P(8)—O(7) | 1.44 Å |
| Ti(1)—Cl(4) | 2.24 Å | P(8)—Cl(9) | 1.93 Å |
| Ti(1)—Cl(5) | 2.23 Å | P(8)—Cl(10) | 1.98 Å |
| Ti(1)—Cl(6) | 2.20 Å | P(8)—Cl(11) | 1.96 Å |

Bond angles:

| | | | |
|---|---|---|---|
| Cl(2)—Ti(1)—Cl(3) | 78.5° | Cl(5)—Ti(1)—Cl(6) | 97.4° |
| Cl(2)—Ti(1)—Cl(5) | 92.8° | Cl(5)—Ti(1)—O(7) | 88.1° |
| Cl(2)—Ti(1)—Cl(6) | 92.2° | Ti(1)—O(7)—P(8) | 151.8° |
| Cl(2)—Ti(1)—O(7) | 83.0° | O(7)—P(8)—Cl(9) | 115.6° |
| Cl(3)—Ti(1)—Cl(4) | 89.1° | O(7)—P(8)—Cl(10) | 111.3° |
| Cl(3)—Ti(1)—Cl(6) | 91.7° | O(7)—P(8)—Cl(11) | 111.5° |
| Cl(3)—Ti(1)—O(7) | 82.2° | Cl(9)—P(8)—Cl(10) | 107.0° |
| Cl(4)—Ti(1)—Cl(5) | 98.2° | Cl(9)—P(8)—Cl(11) | 106.6° |
| Cl(4)—Ti(1)—Cl(6) | 96.2° | Cl(10)—P(8)—Cl(11) | 104.1° |
| Cl(4)—Ti(1)—O(7) | 87.4° | | |

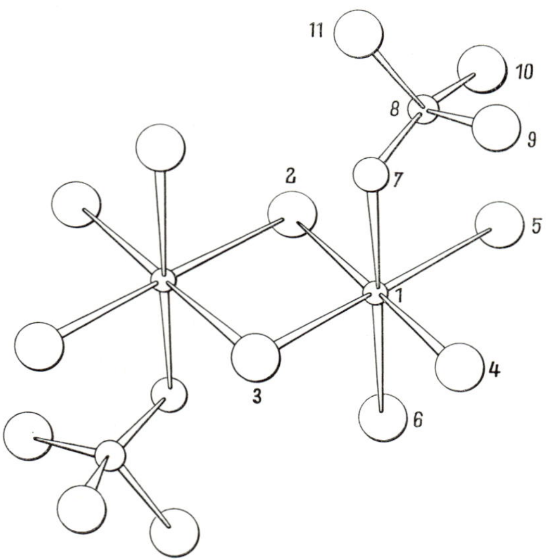


Fig. 9. The structure of $(TiCl_4 \cdot POCl_3)_2$

A few observations can be made, however. Thus it is remarkable that the negative shift in the 1:2 $TiCl_4$ adduct with $POCl_3$ is larger than the negative shift in the corresponding $SnCl_4$ adduct. In the adducts with $(C_6H_5)_3PO$ the effects are reversed (1958: 12; 1959: 10). (We have not been able to suggest any reasonable explanation of this fact.) The negative shift in $NbCl_5 \cdot POCl_3$ is smaller than that in $SbCl_5 \cdot POCl_3$ (1959: 12, 13) a result which is in agreement with the bond lengths presented above. The negative shift in $BiCl_3 \cdot 2POCl_3$ is larger than that in $SbCl_3 \cdot 2POCl_3$ (1959: 12; 1960: 23).

If the two donor-acceptor components give more than one adduct, the negative shift generally increases with increasing mole ratio for acceptor: donor. It is thus larger in $SbCl_3 \cdot (CH_3)_3PO$ than in $SbCl_3 \cdot 2(CH_3)_3PO$ (1960: 23), larger in $HgCl_2 \cdot (C_6H_5)_3PO$ than in $HgCl_2 \cdot 2(C_6H_5)_3PO$ (1959: 11) and larger in $5HgCl_2 \cdot 2(CH_3)_3PO$ than in $HgCl_2 \cdot (CH_3)_3PO$ (1959: 11). On the other hand in the two adducts $TiCl_4 \cdot 2POCl_3$ and $(TiCl_4 \cdot POCl_3)_2$ the shifts are identical (1958: 12).

The negative shifts are very similar in $SbCl_3 \cdot (CH_3)_3PO$ and in $SbCl_5 \cdot$ $\cdot (CH_3)_3PO$ in spite of the great difference between the heats of reaction (p. 63) (1960: 23).

In some cases the negative shifts are larger in the phosphine oxide adducts, and in other cases they are larger in the $POCl_3$ adducts. $SbCl_3$ and $SnCl_4$ are examples of the two different cases (1958: 12; 1959: 12; 1960: 14).

Finally, it has been observed that the P—Cl stretching frequencies are shifted towards higher values in $POCl_3$ adducts (1959: 12; 1962: 15).

**Donor molecules containig the group $>$As$=$O.** The crystal structures of $HgCl_2 \cdot 2(C_6H_5)_3AsO$ (1962: 4) and of $SbCl_3 \cdot 2(C_6H_5)_3AsO$ have been determined (1962: 14).

Bond lengths and bond angles for $HgCl_2 \cdot 2(C_6H_5)_3AsO$ given in Table 6 refer to Figure 10.

Table 6. $HgCl_2 \cdot 2(C_6H_5)_3AsO$

Bond lengths:

| | | | |
|---|---|---|---|
| Hg(1)—Cl(2) | 2.33 Å | As(6)—C(8) | 1.90 Å |
| Hg(1)—Cl(3) | 2.32 Å | As(6)—C(9) | 1.95 Å |
| Hg(1)—O(4) | 2.32 Å | As(6)—C(10) | 1.89 Å |
| Hg(1)—O(5) | 2.37 Å | As(7)—C(11) | 1.92 Å |
| As(6)—O(4) | 1.69 Å | As(7)—C(12) | 1.98 Å |
| As(7)—O(5) | 1.69 Å | As(7)—C(13) | 1.90 Å |

Bond angles:

| | | | |
|---|---|---|---|
| Cl(2)—Hg(1)—Cl(3) | 146.5° | O(4)—As(6)—C(10) | 107.3° |
| Cl(2)—Hg(1)—O(4) | 100.4° | O(5)—As(7)—C(11) | 109.3° |
| Cl(2)—Hg(1)—O(5) | 103.0° | O(5)—As(7)—C(12) | 110.2° |
| Cl(3)—Hg(1)—O(4) | 103.6° | O(5)—As(7)—O(13) | 112.6° |
| Cl(3)—Hg(1)—O(5) | 98.9° | C(8)—As(6)—C(9) | 105.5° |
| O(4)—Hg(1)—O(5) | 92.5° | C(8)—As(6)—C(10) | 110.3° |
| Hg(1)—O(4)—As(6) | 136.7° | C(9)—As(6)—C(10) | 105.9° |
| Hg(1)—O(5)—As(7) | 134.4° | C(11)—As(7)—C(12) | 106.8° |
| O(4)—As(6)—C(8) | 113.8° | C(11)—As(7)—C(13) | 107.3° |
| O(4)—As(6)—C(9) | 113.8° | C(12)—As(7)—C(13) | 110.5° |

The benzene rings are not significantly changed by the adduct formation. The average value for 36 C—C bond lengths is 1.41 Å and the average bond angle C—C—C is 119.7°.

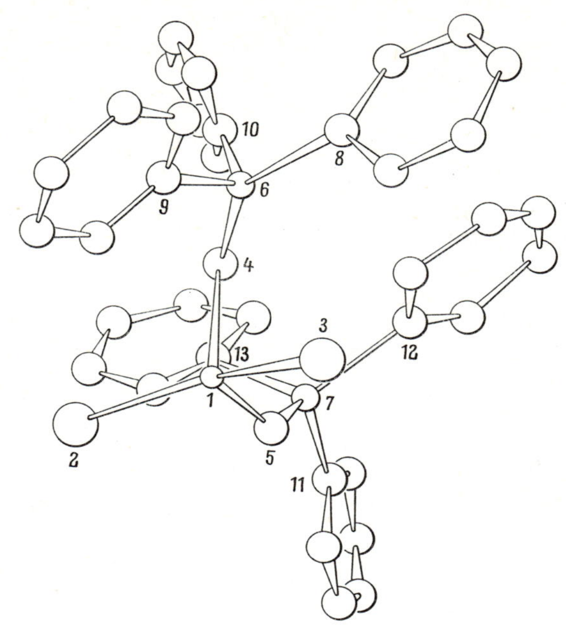


Fig. 10. The structure of $HgCl_2 \cdot 2(C_6H_5)_3AsO$

Bond lengths and bond angles for $SbCl_3 \cdot 2(C_6H_5)_3AsO$ in Table 7 refer to Figure 11.

Table 7. $SbCl_3 \cdot 2(C_6H_5)_3AsO$

Bond lengths:

| | | | |
|---|---|---|---|
| Sb(1)—Cl(2) | 2.59 Å | As(7)—C(9) | 1.91 Å |
| Sb(1)—Cl(3) | 2.59 Å | As(7)—C(10) | 1.94 Å |
| Sb(1)—Cl(4) | 2.20 Å | As(7)—C(11) | 1.94 Å |
| Sb(1)—O(5) | 2.26 Å | As(8)—C(12) | 1.88 Å |
| Sb(1)—O(6) | 2.27 Å | As(8)—C(13) | 1.93 Å |
| As(7)—O(5) | 1.63 Å | As(8)—C(14) | 1.95 Å |
| As(8)—O(6) | 1.68 Å | | |

Bond angles:

| | | | |
|---|---|---|---|
| Cl(2)—Sb(1)—Cl(3) | 93.2° | O(5)—As(7)—C(10) | 109.9° |
| Cl(2)—Sb(1)—Cl(4) | 87.2° | O(5)—As(7)—C(11) | 110.4° |
| Cl(2)—Sb(1)—O(6) | 90.1° | O(6)—As(8)—C(12) | 108.1° |
| Cl(3)—Sb(1)—Cl(4) | 90.0° | O(6)—As(8)—C(13) | 109.4° |
| Cl(3)—Sb(1)—O(5) | 91.1° | O(6)—As(8)—C(14) | 114.8° |
| Cl(4)—Sb(1)—O(5) | 90.4° | C(9)—As(7)—C(10) | 106.2° |
| Cl(4)—Sb(1)—O(6) | 94.3° | C(9)—As(7)—C(11) | 110.3° |
| O(5)—Sb(1)—O(6) | 85.8° | C(10)—As(7)—C(11) | 109.6° |
| Sb(1)—O(5)—As(7) | 140.9° | C(12)—As(8)—C(13) | 107.8° |
| Sb(1)—O(6)—As(8) | 137.2° | C(12)—As(8)—C(14) | 106.1° |
| O(5)—As(7)—C(9) | 110.3° | C(13)—As(8)—C(14) | 110.4° |

The benzene rings are not much influenced by the adduct formation as shown by the average values of the C—C bond length (1.40 Å for 36 bond lengths) and the C—C—C bond angle (119.8° for 36 bond angles).

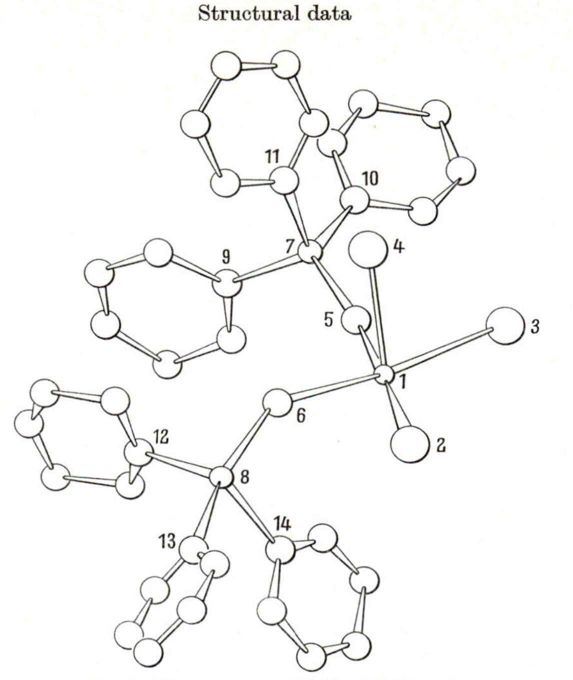


Fig. 11. The structure of $SbCl_3 \cdot 2(C_6H_5)_3AsO$

**Donor molecules containing the group $>S=O$.** Three crystal structure determinations have been carried out. The structures studied are: $BF_3 \cdot (CH_3)_2SO$ (1962: 6), $SbCl_5 \cdot (C_6H_5)_2SO$ (1962: 9) and $SnCl_4 \cdot 2(CH_3)_2SO$ (1962: 8).

Bond lengths and bond angles for $BF_3 \cdot (CH_3)_3SO$ given in Table 8 refer to Figure 12.

Table 8. $BF_3 \cdot (CH_3)_2SO$

Bond lengths:

| | | | |
|---|---|---|---|
| B(1)—F(2) | 1.38 Å | S(6)—O(5) | 1.52 Å |
| B(1)—F(3) | 1.37 Å | S(6)—C(7) | 1.75 Å |
| B(1)—F(4) | 1.34 Å | S(6)—C(8) | 1.77 Å |
| B(1)—O(5) | 1.54 Å | | |

Bond angles:

| | | | |
|---|---|---|---|
| F(2)—B(1)—F(3) | 106.7° | F(4)—B(1)—O(5) | 105.8° |
| F(2)—B(1)—F(4) | 116.5° | B(1)—O(5)—S(6) | 119.2° |
| F(2)—B(1)—O(5) | 107.7° | O(5)—S(6)—C(7) | 103.1° |
| F(3)—B(1)—F(4) | 114.0° | O(5)—S(6)—C(8) | 99.7° |
| F(3)—B(1)—O(5) | 105.3° | C(7)—S(6)—C(8) | 99.7° |

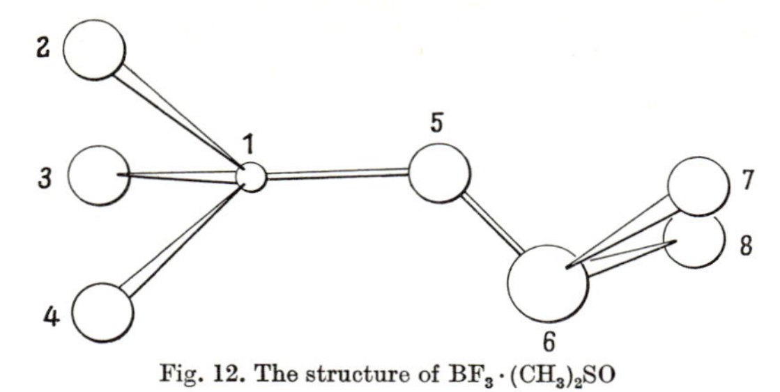

Fig. 12. The structure of $BF_3 \cdot (CH_3)_2SO$

Bond lengths and bond angles for $SbCl_5 \cdot (C_6H_5)_2SO$ given in Table 9 refer to Figure 13.

Table 9. $SbCl_5 \cdot (C_6H_5)_2SO$

Bond lengths:

| | | | |
|---|---|---|---|
| Sb(1)—Cl(2) | 2.33 Å | Sb(1)—O(7) | 2.16 Å |
| Sb(1)—Cl(3) | 2.35 Å | S(8)—O(7) | 1.53 Å |
| Sb(1)—Cl(4) | 2.36 Å | S(8)—C(9) | 1.81 Å |
| Sb(1)—Cl(5) | 2.33 Å | S(8)—C(10) | 1.72 Å |
| Sb(1)—Cl(6) | 2.38 Å | | |

Bond angles:

| | | | |
|---|---|---|---|
| Cl(2)—Sb(1)—Cl(3) | 93.2° | Cl(4)—Sb(1)—Cl(6) | 88.3° |
| Cl(2)—Sb(1)—Cl(4) | 92.7° | Cl(4)—Sb(1)—O(7) | 88.6° |
| Cl(2)—Sb(1)—Cl(5) | 92.8° | Cl(5)—Sb(1)—O(7) | 86.0° |
| Cl(2)—Sb(1)—Cl(6) | 94.9° | Cl(6)—Sb(1)—O(7) | 86.3° |
| Cl(3)—Sb(1)—Cl(5) | 89.6° | Sb(1)—O(7)—S(8) | 117° |
| Cl(3)—Sb(1)—Cl(6) | 90.0° | O(7)—S(8)—C(9) | 105° |
| Cl(3)—Sb(1)—O(7) | 85.5° | O(7)—S(8)—C(10) | 99° |
| Cl(4)—Sb(1)—Cl(5) | 91.3° | C(9)—S(8)—C(10) | 103° |

The benzene rings are not much influenced by the adduct formation as shown by the average C—C bond length (1.41 Å for 12 bond lengths) and C—C—C bond angle (120° for 12 bond angles).

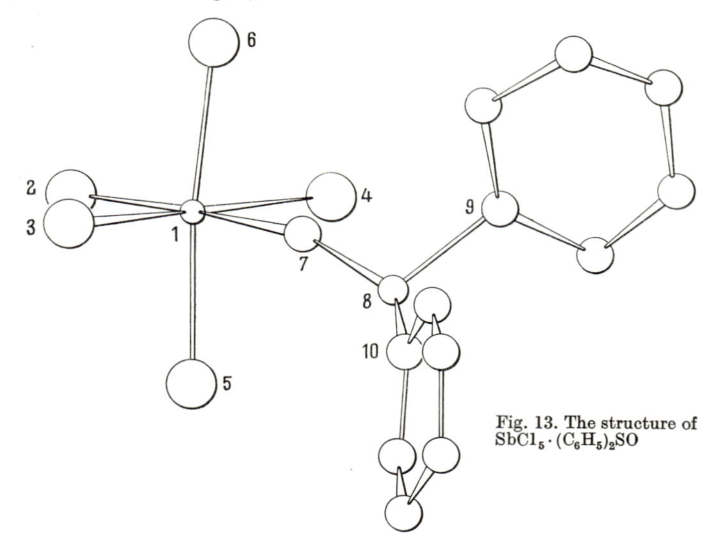

Fig. 13. The structure of $SbCl_5 \cdot (C_6H_5)_2SO$

Bond lengths and bond angles for $SnCl_4 \cdot 2(CH_3)_2SO$ given in Table 10 refer to Figure 14.

Table 10. $SnCl_4 \cdot 2(CH_3)_2SO$

Bond lengths:

| | | | |
|---|---|---|---|
| Sn(1)—Cl(2) | 2.44 Å | S(8)—O(6) | 1.51 Å |
| Sn(1)—Cl(3) | 2.36 Å | S(9)—O(7) | 1.54 Å |
| Sn(1)—Cl(4) | 2.42 Å | S(8)—C(10) | 1.91 Å |
| Sn(1)—Cl(5) | 2.47 Å | S(8)—C(11) | 1.69 Å |
| Sn(1)—O(6) | 2.17 Å | S(9)—C(12) | 1.71 Å |
| Sn(1)—O(7) | 2.10 Å | S(9)—C(13) | 1.86 Å |

Bond angles:

| | | | |
|---|---|---|---|
| Cl(2)—Sn(1)—Cl(3) | 95.9° | Cl(5)—Sn(1)—O(7) | 87.2° |
| Cl(2)—Sn(1)—Cl(4) | 100.8° | O(6)—Sn(1)—O(7) | 87.3° |
| Cl(2)—Sn(1)—Cl(5) | 89.8° | Sn(1)—O(6)—S(8) | 121° |
| Cl(2)—Sn(1)—O(7) | 84.1° | Sn(1)—O(7)—S(9) | 126° |
| Cl(3)—Sn(1)—Cl(4) | 92.4° | O(6)—S(8)—C(10) | 103° |
| Cl(3)—Sn(1)—O(6) | 82.6° | O(6)—S(8)—C(11) | 105° |
| Cl(3)—Sn(1)—O(7) | 86.1° | C(10)—S(8)—C(11) | 116° |
| Cl(4)—Sn(1)—Cl(5) | 93.7° | O(7)—S(9)—C(12) | 110° |
| Cl(4)—Sn(1)—O(6) | 87.8° | O(7)—S(9)—C(13) | 97° |
| Cl(5)—Sn(1)—O(6) | 90.7° | C(12)—S(9)—C(13) | 107° |

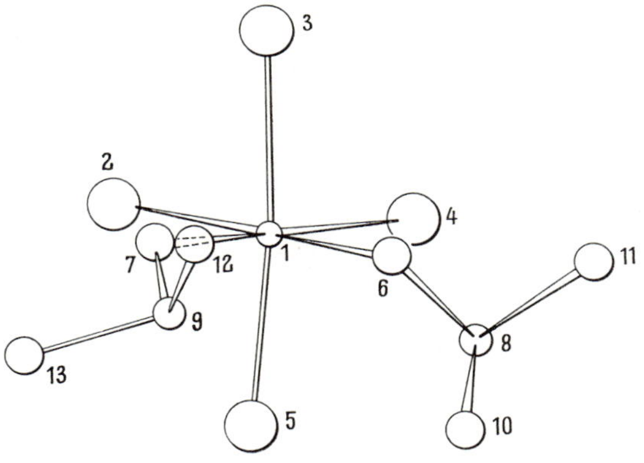

Fig. 14. The structure of $SnCl_4 \cdot 2(CH_3)_2SO$

Infrared studies of $(CH_3)_2SO$ adducts demonstrate that the negative shift of the S=O stretching frequency is of the order of 100 $cm^{-1}$ (1960: 34; 1961: 28). The negative shift is larger for $(CH_3)_2SO$ adducts than for the corresponding $(C_6H_5)_2SO$ adducts (1961: 28).

It has been observed that the vibration frequencies of the adjacent C—S bonds increase in parallel with the decrease of the S=O vibration (1961: 5). This conclusion is in doubt, however, at least for $SnCl_4 \cdot 2(C_6H_5)_2SO$ (1961: 28).

**Donor molecules containing the group $>S\langle^{O}_{O}$.** The crystal structure of $SbCl_5 \cdot (CH_3)_2SO_2$ has been determined (1962: 10).

Bond lengths and bond angles for $SbCl_5 \cdot (CH_3)_2SO_2$ given in Table 11 refer to Figure 15.

Table 11. $SbCl_5 \cdot (CH_3)_2SO_2$

Bond lengths:

| | | | |
|---|---|---|---|
| Sb(1)—Cl(2) | 2.32 Å | Sb(1)—O(7) | 2.12 Å |
| Sb(1)—Cl(3) | 2.26 Å | S(8)—O(7) | 1.53 Å |
| Sb(1)—Cl(4) | 2.34 Å | S(8)—O(9) | 1.46 Å |
| Sb(1)—Cl(5) | 2.32 Å | S(8)—C(10) | 1.79 Å |
| Sb(1)—Cl(6) | 2.37 Å | S(8)—C(11) | 1.60 Å |

Bond angles:

| | | | |
|---|---|---|---|
| Cl(2)—Sb(1)—Cl(3) | 93.3° | Cl(5)—Sb(1)—O(7) | 84.3° |
| Cl(2)—Sb(1)—Cl(4) | 91.3° | Cl(6)—Sb(1)—O(7) | 89.0° |
| Cl(2)—Sb(1)—Cl(5) | 96.2° | Sb(1)—O(7)—S(8) | 138.7° |
| Cl(2)—Sb(1)—Cl(6) | 93.9° | O(7)—S(8)—O(9) | 115° |
| Cl(3)—Sb(1)—Cl(4) | 92.7° | O(7)—S(8)—C(10) | 105° |
| Cl(3)—Sb(1)—Cl(5) | 90.2° | O(7)—S(8)—C(11) | 113° |
| Cl(3)—Sb(1)—O(7) | 83.7° | O(9)—S(8)—C(10) | 107° |
| Cl(4)—Sb(1)—Cl(6) | 87.5° | O(9)—S(8)—C(11) | 115° |
| Cl(4)—Sb(1)—O(7) | 88.4° | C(10)—S(8)—C(11) | 100° |
| Cl(5)—Sb(1)—Cl(6) | 88.7° | | |

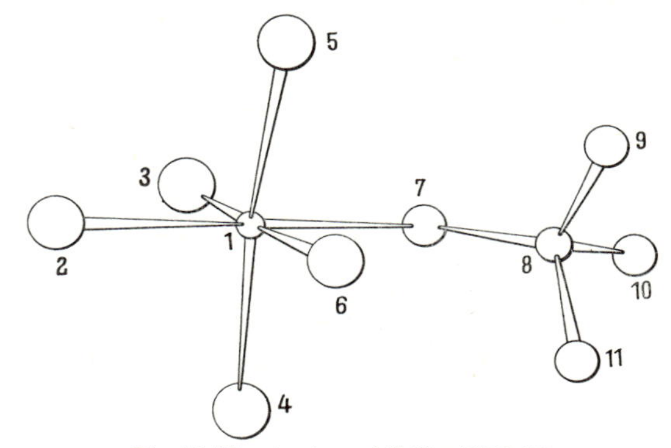


Fig. 15. The structure of $SbCl_5 \cdot (CH_3)_2SO_2$

**Donor molecules containing the group >Se=O.** The crystal structures of $SnCl_4 \cdot 2SeOCl_2$ (1960: 9) and $SbCl_5 \cdot SeOCl_2$ (1962: 12) have been determined.

Bond lengths and bond angles for $SnCl_4 \cdot 2SeOCl_2$ given in Table 12 refer to Figure 16.

Table 12. $SnCl_4 \cdot 2SeOCl_2$

Bond lengths:

| | | | |
|---|---|---|---|
| Sn(1)—Cl(2) | 2.36 Å | Se(5)—O(4) | 1.73 Å |
| Sn(1)—Cl(3) | 2.41 Å | Se(5)—Cl(6) | 2.13 Å |
| Sn(1)—O(4) | 2.12 Å | Se(5)—Cl(7) | 2.14 Å |

Bond angles:

| | | | |
|---|---|---|---|
| Cl(2)—Sn(1)—Cl(3) | 95.1° | O(4)—Sn(1)—O(10) | 81.9° |
| Cl(2)—Sn(1)—O(4) | 89.1° | Sn(1)—O(4)—Se(5) | 121.5° |
| Cl(2)—Sn(1)—Cl(8) | 100.1° | O(4)—Se(5)—Cl(6) | 98.9° |
| Cl(2)—Sn(1)—Cl(9) | 95.0° | O(4)—Se(5)—Cl(8) | 103.3° |
| Cl(3)—Sn(1)—O(4) | 86.2° | Cl(6)—Se(5)—Cl(7) | 97.6° |
| Cl(3)—Sn(1)—O(10) | 81.9° | | |

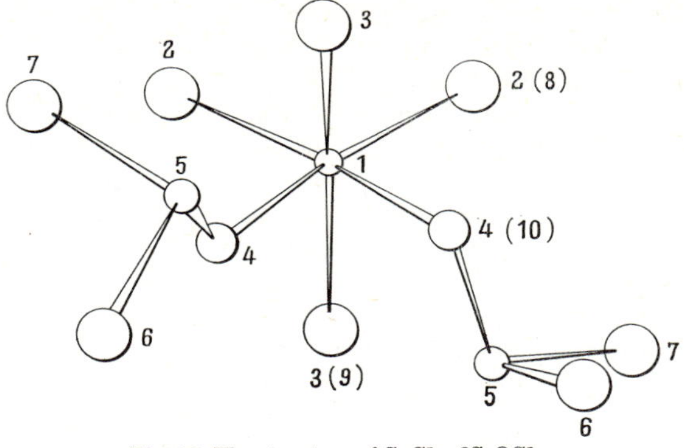


Fig. 16. The structure of $SnCl_4 \cdot 2SeOCl_2$

Bond lengths and bond angles for $SbCl_5 \cdot SeOCl_2$ given in Table 13 refer to Figure 17. The structure contains two structurally independent molecules and corresponding values for the two molecules are given in parallel.

Table 13. $SbCl_5 \cdot SeOCl_2$

Bond lengths:

|  | | |
|---|---|---|
| Sb(1)—Cl(2) | 2.33 Å | 2.33 Å |
| Sb(1)—Cl(3) | 2.33 Å | 2.36 Å |
| Sb(1)—Cl(4) | 2.35 Å | 2.32 Å |
| Sb(1)—Cl(5) | 2.36 Å | 2.33 Å |
| Sb(1)—Cl(6) | 2.33 Å | 2.33 Å |
| Sb(1)—O(7) | 2.15 Å | 2.04 Å |
| Se(8)—O(7) | 1.63 Å | 1.72 Å |
| Se(8)—Cl(9) | 2.10 Å | 2.11 Å |
| Se(8)—Cl(10) | 2.13 Å | 2.12 Å |

Bond angles:

|  | | |
|---|---|---|
| Cl(2)—Sb(1)—Cl(4) | 94.5° | 96.8° |
| Cl(2)—Sb(1)—Cl(5) | 90.6° | 91.5° |
| Cl(2)—Sb(1)—Cl(6) | 90.4° | 89.9° |
| Cl(2)—Sb(1)—O(7) | 86.0° | 84.2° |
| Cl(3)—Sb(1)—Cl(4) | 93.3° | 92.2° |
| Cl(3)—Sb(1)—Cl(5) | 88.0° | 88.0° |
| Cl(3)—Sb(1)—Cl(6) | 90.1° | 89.5° |
| Cl(3)—Sb(1)—O(7) | 86.2° | 86.8° |
| Cl(4)—Sb(1)—Cl(5) | 92.4° | 94.2° |
| Cl(4)—Sb(1)—Cl(6) | 94.2° | 93.4° |
| Cl(5)—Sb(1)—O(7) | 87.1° | 85.5° |
| Cl(6)—Sb(1)—O(7) | 86.3° | 86.9° |
| Sb(1)—O(7)—Se(8) | 120.9° | 121.7° |
| O(7)—Se(8)—Cl(9) | 101.4° | 102.5° |
| O(7)—Se(8)—Cl(10) | 97.0° | 98.8° |
| Cl(9)—Se(8)—Cl(10) | 98.6° | 98.9° |

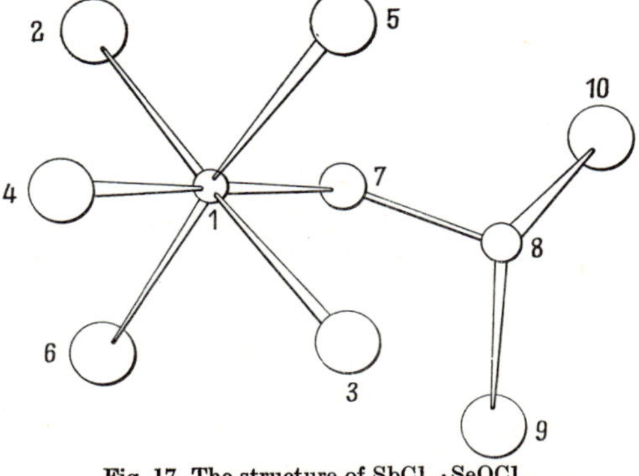


Fig. 17. The structure of $SbCl_5 \cdot SeOCl_2$

The infrared studies of $SnCl_4 \cdot 2SeOCl_2$ and $TiCl_4 \cdot 2SeOCl_2$ show that the negative shift of the Se = O stretching frequency is larger in the $TiCl_4$ adduct than in the $SnCl_4$ adduct (1959: 10).

**Coordination around the acceptor atom.** X-ray studies show that in a number of adducts, which can be described as having octahedral coordination, the coordination around the acceptor atom shows a deviation from the regular octahedral configuration. These deviations can be interpreted as being due to *two steric factors*, namely the van der Waals radii of the ligand atoms and their distances from the central atom. This important result has been firmly established by the structural studies (1962: 32). The results will be discussed here in some detail, since the conclusions are probably valid for other types of coordination.

The first piece of experimental evidence to be discussed is that provided by the bond angles in a number of 1:1 adducts of $SbCl_5$ with different donor molecules. From Fig. 15, since the van der Waals radius of the oxygen atom is much smaller than that of the chlorine atom, it is quite clear which type of deformation of the regular coordination is to be expected. The nearest chlorine atoms will fall in against the Sb—O bond, and in Table 14 the average values of these Cl—Sb—O bond angles are shown together with the averaged values for the Cl—Sb—Cl bond angles and the $Cl^x$—Sb—Cl bond angles where $Cl^x$ stands for the chlorine atoms opposite to the donor-acceptor bond. The different adducts are given in the order of increasing Sb—O bond lengths. It can be seen that the ex-

Table 14. *Bond angles around the acceptor atom in* $SbCl_5 \cdot D$ *and* $SnCl_4 \cdot 2D$ *adducts*

| | D | | | | |
|---|---|---|---|---|---|
| $SbCl_5 \cdot D$ | $(CH_3)_3PO$ | $(CH_3)_2SO_2$ | $SeOCl_2$ | $(C_6H_5)_2SO$ | $POCl_3$ |
| Sb—O in Å | 1.94 | 2.12 | 2.15 | 2.16 | 2.17 |
| Cl—Sb—O | 88.3° | 86.4° | 86.3° | 86.7° | 85.3° |
| Cl—Sb—Cl | 90.0° | 89.8° | 89.8° | 89.8° | 89.6° |
| $Cl^x$—Sb—Cl | 91.8° | 93.7° | 93.9° | 93.4° | 94.7° |

| | D | |
|---|---|---|
| $SnCl_4 \cdot 2D$ | $SeOCl_2$ | $POCl_3$ |
| Sn—O in Å | 2.12 | 2.28 |
| O—Sn—O | 81.9° | 78.3° |
| Cl—Sn—O | 84.1° | 83.0° |
| $Cl^x$—Sn—O | 89.1° | 89.4° |
| $Cl^x$—Sn—Cl | 95.1° | 95.6° |
| $Cl^x$—Sn—$Cl^x$ | 100.1° | 103.0° |

pected deviations from regular octahedral coordination occur, and also that the effect is greater for a longer Sb—O bond length. The standard deviations of the bond lengths are such that only the differences between 1.94 Å and the three other values can be considered as significant. As the oxygen atom approaches the antimony atom, the chlorine atoms return to a more regular octahedral configuration. The bond angles in $NbCl_5 \cdot POCl_3$ are also consistent with this model (Table 2). The same effect is shown for two 1:2 adducts of $SnCl_4$ in Table 14. In this instance distinctions are drawn between the bond angles, O—Sn—O, Cl—Sn—O, $Cl^x$—Sn—O, Cl—Sn—Cl, $Cl^x$—Sn—Cl and $Cl^x$—Sn—$Cl^x$ (see Fig. 16, for example). The deviations from regular octahedral coordination are again in agreement with predictions based on the assumption of two simple steric effects. Finally it should be mentioned that the effect of varying bond length is well demonstrated in $(TiCl_4 \cdot POCl_3)_2$ where the two bridging chlorine atoms are much further from the titanium atom, and can therefore form bonds with a very small angle (Fig. 9).

Other steric factors can of course alter the conditions. Thus in $SnCl_4 \cdot 2(CH_3)_2SO$ (Fig. 14) a carbon atom prevents the two oxygen atoms approaching each other as closely as might be expected from a comparison with the other 1:2 adducts of $SnCl_4$.

Finally, the large deviations from regular *tetrahedral* coordination found in $HgCl_2 \cdot 2(C_6H_5)_3AsO$ can also be explained in terms of the small size of the oxygen atom *and* its comparatively great distance from the mercury atom.

These steric effects are the net result of electronic repulsions both from the lone pairs of electrons on the chlorine and oxygen atoms and from the bonding electrons. There is no reason for thinking, as some authors have done, that the only significant repulsions are those between the bonding electron pairs.

**The structures of the donor molecules.** The structure of a given donor molecule varies little between adducts with different acceptor molecules. Any deviation from a regular configuration which is found in more than one adduct is therefore of interest, even if in each instance, the deviation from regularity is not mathematically significant.

The deviations from trigonal symmetry found in $POCl_3 \cdot (CH_3)_3PO$ and $(C_6H_5)_3AsO$ are very small, and will therefore be given no further consideration.

However, all donors which contain lone pairs of electrons and which are therefore less symmetrical exhibit in the adduct structures common trends which should be noted.

The structure of $SnCl_4 \cdot 2SeOCl_2$ serves to illustrate this point. Chlorine atoms, on the side of the selenium atoms from which ligands are absent, are located at appreciably shorter distances than those expected on the basis of van der Waals packing distances. This finding applies to chlorine atoms both from the same and from adjacent molecules. Figure 18 shows the "secondary" interaction of the selenium atom in $SeOCl_2$ as it occurs in the adduct $SnCl_4 \cdot 2SeOCl_2$. It is seen that the configuration corresponds to distorted octahedral coordination. Similar effects are found in the other adducts of sulfoxides and $SeOCl_2$.

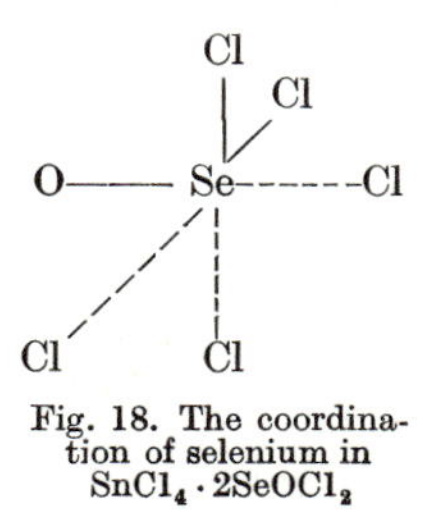

Fig. 18. The coordination of selenium in $SnCl_4 \cdot 2SeOCl_2$

**Comments on spectroscopic observations.** In a great number of cases where negative shifts of vibration frequencies have been reported, a simultaneous splitting of the lines has been observed. This splitting has often been explained as being due to the existence of two types of bonds between the acceptor and the donor atoms, or to the coupling of two vibrations in 1:2 adducts. However, many observations demonstrate that this cannot be the only cause. Thus splitting is observed in $SeOCl_2 \cdot 2SeOCl_2$, which contains two structurally equivalent donor molecules, and still more important is its detection in 1:1 adducts of $SbCl_5$. The effect has been studied in some detail in instances of very weak interaction (1959: 12) and it seems fair to conclude that this is a point in need of further experimental and theoretical clarification.

## 23. Charge distribution

This heading covers all experimental evidence relating to the charge distribution in adduct molecules compared with that in the donor or acceptor molecules.

### a) Dipole moment studies

The classical method of studying charge distribution is to determine dipole moments from measurements of dielectric constants. Results obtained by this method are generally not very accurate unless the measurements have been made in the gas phase at different temperatures. Assuming, temporarily, that dipole moments could be determined accurately, a knowledge of the structures of the adduct and its components would also be necessary before firm conclusions regarding the charge distribution in the adduct molecule and the donor-acceptor bond could be drawn.

In connection with these studies two difficulties have generally been overlooked. Thus the charge distribution in the donor molecule is often altered by adduct formation. In addition the dipole moment vector for the donor molecule is not necessarily parallel with the donor-acceptor bond direction, as has generally been assumed. (A recent discussion (1958: 7) provides the only exception.) The latter important restriction may be due to lack of coincidence between the directions of the oxo-bond and the dipole moment of the donor molecule. Alternatively, it might arise through the departure from $180^0$ in the bond angle at the oxygen atom, and as was shown in the preceding chapter, such departures do occur.

The results briefly referred to in the following discussion do not permit any firm conclusions regarding the charge distribution in the adduct molecule.

An obvious result of the dipole moment studies is to establish that a strong dipole moment increment occurs in association with adduct formation. The measurements have been made under very different conditions, however, and there is little purpose in an uncritical listing of the dipole moments which have been reported. References are, however, given to studies with different acceptor molecules; a few comments will then be made regarding possible conclusions. The following acceptor molecules have been studied: $BF_3$ (1958: 7), $AlCl_3$ (1932: 4; 1941: 4), $AlBr_3$ (1932: 4; 1943: 5; 1958: 13), $GaCl_3$ (1941: 1), $SnCl_4$ (1932: 7; 1946: 6; 1956: 10; 1957: 23), $TiCl_4$ (1956: 10; 1960: 60), $ZrCl_4$ (1957: 31; 1959: 19), $ZrBr_4$

(1959: 20) and $ZrI_4$ (1959: 42). Adducts of transition metal halides with phosphine oxides have also been studied (1960: 12).

There are indications that the dipole moment increment is larger for $AlCl_3$ than for $AlBr_3$ while the increments for $BF_3$ and $GaCl_3$ are still smaller. In the same way the increment is larger for $SnCl_4$ than for $ZrCl_4$ in corresponding 1:2 adducts and larger for $TiCl_4$ than for $ZrCl_4$ in 1:1 adducts.

Some 1:1 adducts of $TiCl_4$ and $ZrCl_4$ constitute a special interest since dipole moments have been reported for these compounds although none should be observed if their structures are similar to that of $(TiCl_4 \cdot POCl_3)_2$. In these instances the dipole moments might be due to dissociation in the solvents used, or to the formation of less symmetrical dimeric molecules. The latter possibility must be included in view of the three different modifications found for $TiCl_4 \cdot POCl_3$.

The high dipole moments of all the 1:2 adducts studied indicate that they are *cis* adducts, a result also obtained from structure determinations.

The large dipole moment increment makes it possible to carry out good dielectric titrations in many cases (1956: 31; 1961: 47). (Using megacycle-frequency oscillators this can be combined with conductimetric titration (1962: 26).)

## b) Nuclear resonance methods

Modern NMR methods permit measurements of chemical shifts and of quadrupole coupling constants. Both these quantities give information regarding the charge distribution but in each case a straightforward interpretation is difficult, a point which has been made in every discussion of this technique. Thus we know that the PMR chemical shift does not give a direct picture of the changes in charge distribution associated with the formation of hydrogen bonds, and we also know that changes in hybridization influence the quadrupole coupling constants. Since NMR methods have been used very little to study adduct molecules a detailed discussion is unnecessary. It is hoped, however, that discussion of the chemical bonds present in adduct molecules will encourage the application of the NMR technique to this field.

In fact the only study of chemical shifts which has been reported has led to very puzzling results: $BF_3 \cdot CH_3COOC_2H_5$ has been investigated by PMR methods (1961: 7). If the chemical shifts depended only upon the electron density, the results would indicate an increase in the electron density about the hydrogen atoms of the methylene group in $—OCH_2CH_3$ in consequence of adduct formation. This interpretation is untenable, and it becomes necessary to take into account the influence of the $C=O$ bond on the magnetic properties.

A quadrupole moment study has also been reported, namely that on $SnCl_4 \cdot C_6H_5NO_2$ (1953: 13). The quadrupole resonance frequency for $Cl^{35}$ is shifted from 24.09 Mc/sec in $SnCl_4$ to 23.08 Mc/sec in the adduct. This indicates a decrease in the charge asymmetry about the chlorine atoms and a higher polarity for the $Sn—Cl$ bonds. It is noteworthy that in the same paper the $Cl^{35}$ quadrupole resonance frequency for $TiCl_4$ is reported to be only 6.05 Mc/sec.

It should be added that NMR methods have also been used to prove the octahedral *cis* configuration in 1:2 adducts of $SnF_4$ and $TiF_4$ using the coupling effects on the $F^{19}$ resonance (1960: 28), and to prove that in the adduct between $BCl_3$ and $HCON(CH_3)_2$ the latter molecule has a planar structure (1960: 26).

### c) Chemical evidence

It seems fair to say that so far most of our knowledge about the electron distribution in adduct molecules has been obtained from purely chemical studies. The possible relationships between the electron densities about the donor oxygen atoms and the heats of reactions for the donor-acceptor bond lengths will be discussed in the theoretical section. In this section, reference will be made to more direct evidence regarding electron density changes in adducts with nitromethane. Thus it has recently been found that in a 2% solution of $AlCl_3$ in $CH_3NO_2$, anthracene is readily converted into the monovalent positive ion. The resulting blue-green solution exhibits electron spin resonance, and the UV absorption spectrum is identical with that of the monovalent anthracene ion (1960: 61).

The same increased electron affinity arising from electron density withdrawal on adduct formation can be expected for the carbon atom in carbonyl compounds. An early theory developed by Pfeiffer (1911: 1) suggested that in some ternary compounds such as
$SnCl_4 \cdot 2C_6H_4(OH)CHO \cdot 2H_2O$ and $SnCl_4 \cdot 2(CH{=}CHC_6H_5)_2CO \cdot C_6H_6$, the third type of molecule is added to the carbonyl carbon atom. Adduct formation of this kind is of considerable importance in the use of acceptor molecules as catalysts.

## 24. Decomposition of adduct molecules

Anyone with practical experience of adduct formation with organic donor molecules knows that irreversible decomposition reactions often complicate the preparation of well-defined, crystalline adducts. This is important in connection with the use of acceptor halides as catalysts, and some applications will be considered in the next chapter. Decomposition of this type will be considered, initially, as a "complication" of adduct chemistry, and some possible elimination reactions will be mentioned without any attempt being made to cover all the experimental observations of possible decompositions.

### a) Elimination of hydrogen chloride

The simplest case is the elimination of HCl in reactions between acceptor halides and carboxylic acids or other oxo-acids as donors. This type of reaction is similar to the hydrolysis of the halides and needs no detailed exemplification. The halides that fume in air, such as $SbCl_5$, $SnCl_4$ and $BCl_3$, generally react at room temperature, whereas $BF_3$, $ZnCl_2$

and $HgCl_2$ show less tendency to decompose in this way at moderate temperatures. Intermediate products have been isolated and one of the more remarkable is $Cl_4SbOCOCOOSbCl_4$, obtained by reaction between $SbCl_5$ and oxalic acid (1902: 4). Many other examples have been reported (1902: 4; 1907: 4; 1925: 1; 1927: 5).

The elimination of HCl can also be effected with amides in which the hydrogen atoms bonded to nitrogen are acidic (1910: 6). A recent example is the gradual decomposition of $BCl_3 \cdot RCONH_2$ where the first stage of elimination is $BCl_3 \cdot RCONH_2 \rightarrow BCl_2NHCOR + HCl$, followed by $BCl_2NHCOR \rightarrow BCl = NCOR + HCl$ (1960: 37).

The possibility of HCl elimination with enol forms of diketones or ketoesters is obvious, and such decomposition reactions have also been reported (1903: 2, 8; 1955: 4). Intermediate decomposition products such as $SnCl_3(CH_3COCHCOOC_2H_5)$ have been identified. Even simple ketones and esters can react in the same way. With $ZrCl_4$ and $(CH_3)_2CO$ a definite adduct still exists at $-5^0$ C, but at room temperature decomposition begins with the formation of $ZrCl_3(CH_2COCH_3)$ and HCl (1959: 18). An intermediate found during a similar decomposition of an ester is $Cl_4SbCH_2OCOCOOCH_2SbCl_4$ (1902: 4). In some cases eliminations of this type are thought to be responsible for complications in Friedel-Craft acylations with $CH_3COCl$ (1901: 1).

### b) Other elimination reactions

Molecules other than HCl can be eliminated, and the formation of alkyl halides has been reported in many cases. Thus adducts of esters with $ZrCl_4$ or $HfCl_4$ decompose at $125^0$ C (for the ethyl benzoate); the first reaction is thought to be $ZrCl_4 \cdot 2C_6H_5COOC_2H_5 \rightarrow ZrCl_2(C_6H_5COO)_2 + 2C_2H_5Cl$. The intermediate zirconium compound becomes resinous at higher temperatures and finally chars at $225^0$ C. A number of similar decompositions have been studied (1934: 5; 1940: 2; 1952: 9; 1954: 8; 1958: 23). Adducts with esters of phosphoric acid exhibit similar reactions, one example being the decomposition of $SnCl_4 \cdot 2(C_2H_5O)_3PO$ to $SnCl_2[(C_2H_5O)_2PO_2]_2$ and $2C_2H_5Cl$ (1952: 17).

Finally, $CH_4$ can be eliminated as in $2Ga(CH_3)_3 \cdot CH_3COOH \rightarrow = [Ga(CH_3)_2(CH_3COO)]_2 + 2CH_4$ (1953: 6).

### c) Exchange reactions

The above elimination reactions could have been expressed formally as exchange reactions between $Cl^-$ and the various anions, and a further possibility is offered by exchange with the alkoxide ion of an ester instead of with the carboxylate anion. This reaction is reported for $BCl_3 \cdot RCOOR'$ which decomposes to $RCOCl$ and $BCl_2OR'$. The rather intricate pattern of complete decomposition has been discussed in detail (1955: 2; 1956: 8). The decomposition of $SiCl_4$ adducts with phosphates is simpler and leads to $POCl_3$ and silicates (1961: 48).

More complicated reactions, formally corresponding to full or partial exchange between oxygen and chlorine, have also been reported. One such reaction: $SiX_4 \cdot 2(C_6H_5)_2SO = SiO_2 + 2(C_6H_5)_2SX_2$ has been studied in detail. This proceeds via a series of silicon oxide halides but the final product is $SiO_2$ (1960: 62; 1961: 28). The partial formation of halogenated ethers by the decomposition of $BCl_3 \cdot RCHO$ represents a more intricate case (1957: 14).

Further details of reactions of this type are given in a recent book: W. GERRARD, The organic chemistry of boron, Academic Press, London 1961 and in a review article (1958: 40).

### d) Condensation reactions

Many decomposition reactions are related to the acid-catalyzed aldol condensation. Although considered in the next chapter, they must be mentioned here since they are undoubtedly responsible for complications in adduct preparation. The condensation of ketones in the presence of $ZnCl_2$ provides the simplest example. Thus, acetophenone is easily condensed:

$$2C_6H_5COCH_3 \rightarrow \overset{CH_3}{\underset{C_6H_5}{>}}C = CHCOC_6H_5 + H_2O$$

(1912 : 1). This stage does not represent the end of the reaction and more highly condensed products are obtained. Similar reactions occur in the presence of $BeCl_2$ (1925: 4). Complex products have been reported in a recent study in which $BF_3$ was used as a catalyst (1957: 13). Reactions of this type are also experienced by aldehydes, particularly those containing hydrogen atoms in the position $\alpha$ to the aldehyde group. This is probably the reason why adducts with benzaldehyde are sometimes stated to be more stable than adducts with aliphatic aldehydes. No clear distinction is made between thermal stability towards dissociation to the components and stability towards decomposition reactions.

Condensation reactions lead to a release of water molecules, and hydrolysis is subsequently effected by acceptor halides which are themselves hydrolyzed. An example is provided by the reaction $SiCl_4 + 8(CH_3)_2CO \rightarrow Si(OH)_4 + 4HCl + 4(CH_3)_2C = CHCOCH_3$ (1913: 6).

An alternative initial reaction is represented by a possible interaction between $BCl_3$ and aldehydes: $BCl_3 + RCHO \rightarrow BCl_2OC\begin{smallmatrix} R \\ H \\ Cl \end{smallmatrix}$. According to the authors decomposition does not take place via the adduct in this case (1957: 14). The occurrence of such reactions demonstrates that the isolation of a solid compound with a composition corresponding to that of a definite adduct (a 1:1 adduct in this case) does not prove that an adduct exists. Some of the compounds included in the systematic treatment might be of this type.

The reduction of ketones with $B_2H_6$ is thought to proceed via a similar compound

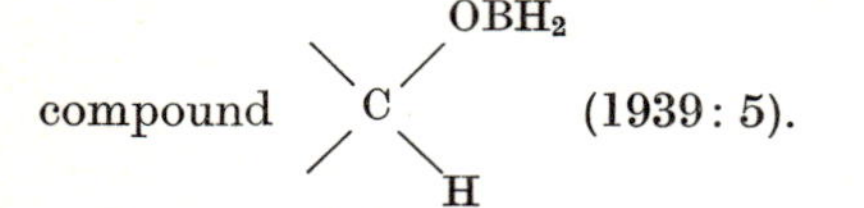

(1939: 5).

## 25. The catalytical activity of acceptor molecules

Acceptor molecules have been widely used as catalysts for different organic reactions but a survey of this field is not within the scope of this book. Some points intimately connected with the formation of adduct molecules will be briefly mentioned, mainly for the benefit of the reader with little knowledge of organic chemistry.

A most important question is whether molecular amounts of acceptor molecules are needed for catalytic activity. (It is somewhat doubtful if the term catalyst is applicable if molecular amounts are necessary, but this is a rather academic point.) This basic problem is clearly presented by CAMPBELL and ELEY (1944: 6) in the form of two thought-provoking questions: Is adduct formation necessary to make the reaction thermodynamically favourable? Is the adduct thus formed catalytically active? Some attempts have been made to answer these questions but conclusive results have not been obtained so far.

### a) Friedel-Craft acylation

Friedel-Craft reactions provide the most important field of application for acceptor molecules and speculations concerning the role of adduct formation in these reactions made an early appearance (1893: 1). In this connection *acylation* reactions are of particular interest, since according to an early suggestion, now regarded as confirmed by spectroscopic studies, they might involve adducts with oxo-compounds. Thus it has been shown that $AlCl_3 \cdot C_6H_5COCl$ and $AlCl_3 \cdot (C_6H_5)_2CO$ are both intermediates in the Friedel-Craft acylation of benzene (1954: 2). Although the detailed mechanism is not firmly established, it appears fundamentally different from that of the familiar Friedel-Craft *alkylation* where, in general, oxo-compounds are not involved (see, however, p. 84). This is also evident from the finding that the yield for the reaction between $C_6H_5COCl$ and $C_6H_6$ increases with the amount of $AlCl_3$ or $FeCl_3$ employed as catalyst, while the corresponding alkylation reaction with $C_6H_5CH_2Cl$ is independent of catalyst concentration (1930:7; 1935:1). The actual complexity of this reaction is demonstrated by the fact that mixed catalysts $AlCl_3$—$FeCl_3$ give a stronger effect than either of the pure components (1935:1).

The yield studies have been critizied by BROWN and JENSEN (1958: 41) who made careful kinetic studies of the reaction $C_6H_5COCl + C_6H_6 \rightarrow (C_6H_5)_2CO + HCl$ in benzoyle chloride employing $AlCl_3$ as the catalyst. (Later studies in other solvents (1959: 58) gave different results.) The reaction was found to be of the second order with the rate $= k[AlCl_3][C_6H_6]$ and some possible reaction mechanisms were suggested. The main feature of one of the proposed mechanisms is a nucleophilic attack of benzene on the carbon atom of the adduct formed with the acyl chloride. Comparative studies with other acceptor molecules demonstrate the following sequence for catalytical efficiency: $SbCl_5 > FeCl_3 > GaCl_3 > AlCl_3 > SnCl_4 > BCl_3 > SbCl_3$ (1958: 42). The mechanisms suggested do not seem very convincing, however. Thus it was implied that $SbCl_5$, $FeCl_3$ and $GaCl_3$ do not exhibit simple second order kinetics because they do not form 1:1 adducts, and the existence of 2:1 adducts of $SbCl_5$ with $(C_6H_5)_2CO$ was mentioned as proof of this. In the systematic treatment, however, it was shown that such compositions are rare (see p. 28) and it seems probable that other reaction mechanisms will be discovered.

It is important to the present discussion to know what type of adduct formation occurs between an acyl halide and an acceptor molecule. Experimental proof for the existence of $RCO^+$ as an intermediate in the acylation reaction has been claimed and in a number of papers this has been correlated with the formation of the salt-like adduct $RCOAlCl_4$ (e. g. 1937: 8; 1954: 19). $RCO^+$ should be an intermediate even in the use of $C_6H_5COCl$, although the solid adduct is not salt-like (p. 13) (1961: 49). Brown and Jensen, on the other hand, claim that adduct formation with oxygen weakens the adjacent C—Cl bond. No support for such a suggestion has been presented and evidence regarding other types of donor indicates that the C — Cl bond is strengthened. It would probably be more useful to base the discussion on electron density variations about the carbon atom rather than on bond strengths since there is no direct reason to assume that equilibrium conditions are of any importance for the activation energies. In view of these uncertainties it seems fair to say that as yet the mechanism of the Friedel-Craft acylation has not been given a theoretical treatment which is in good agreement with the present knowledge of adduct molecules.

Finally, it might be mentioned that self-acylation is sometimes effected with $AlCl_3$ and $GaCl_3$ adducts of acyl halides (1901: 1; 1956: 16).

The situation as regards other types of Friedel-Craft reaction is no clearer. If a carboxylic acid is eliminated instead of HCl, alkylation with esters will result: $HCOOC_3H_7 + C_6H_6 \rightarrow HCOOH + C_6H_5C_3H_7(i)$. This reaction takes place using $AlCl_3$ or $BF_3$ as catalyst, and it has been shown that the yields are proportional to the catalyst concentrations (1937: 9). In this instance any proposed mechanism must explain why the normal propylformate gives an isopropyl derivative of benzene, a result which appears to involve olefines as intermediates. The mechanism which has been suggested is probably wrong since it makes the initial assumption that the bridging oxygen atom of the ester is the donor atom. Similar alkylations can also be effected using alkylcarbonates, alkylsulfates and alkylsilicates (1936: 3).

An interesting observation is that $BF_3$ (generally a rather poor Friedel-Craft catalyst) is very effective if water, alcohols or carboxylic acids are produced, so that strong adducts are formed with this acceptor molecule (1934: 2). $\beta$-diketones have been prepared from ketones and anhydrides in this way $RCOCH_3 + (CH_3CO)_2O = CH_3COOH + RCOCH_2COCH_3$ (1943: 1).

### b) The Gattermann-Koch reaction

A very interesting study has been made of the Gattermann-Koch reaction: $C_6H_6 + CO \rightarrow C_6H_5CHO$.

It was first found that the free energy change in this reaction is highly unfavourable and might even be positive (1949: 7); complex formation between the aldehyde produced and different acceptor molecules is therefore a prerequisite for the reaction. It is self-evident that molecular amounts of acceptor compound are involved and a careful thermochemical study showed that the energy gain due to adduct formation was sufficient to create the thermodynamical conditions required for reaction. CuCl is not very useful for this purpose but appears necessary to bind CO (1949: 8). The kinetics of the reaction have also been studied (1949: 8) but the interpretation is complicated by the presence of HCl in the reaction mixture (formyl chloride is assumed to be the active species). Nevertheless adduct formation seems to be of importance in the kinetics since the order of activity for different acceptor molecules shows some relation to the heats of reaction per donor-acceptor bond formed (see p. 63). This relation is discussed by the authors.

### c) Condensation reactions

The discussion of condensation reactions catalysed by $ZnCl_2$ (see p. 82) will now be continued with an examination of the reaction $(C_6H_5)_2CO + C_6H_5NH_2 \rightarrow (C_6H_5)_2C{=}NC_6H_5$, which has been studied in some detail (1912: 1). In this reaction it is not necessary to use the $ZnCl_2$ catalyst in molecular amounts. Some interesting observations have been made which so far have not received a satisfactory explanation. Thus anile formation does not occur if all the aniline has first reacted with $ZnCl_2$ to form $ZnCl_2 \cdot 2C_6H_5NH_2$ before the addition of benzophenone, while the addition of aniline to the adduct $ZnCl_2 \cdot 2(CH_3)_2CO$ leads to condensation. This would indicate that $ZnCl_2 \cdot 2C_6H_5NH_2$ is the real catalyst and in this connection it has been demonstrated that other amine adducts can also be used. ($ZnCl_2$ alone should give rise to self-condensation of the ketone.) A comparison between different adducts shows that those containing the more ionic bonds are less efficient as catalysts. Thus $ZnSO_4 \cdot 2C_6H_5NH_2$ is not a catalyst. The mechanism suggested is not convincing, but this early investigation might serve as a reminder that much work on adducts was once begun in order to clarify catalytical reactions and it is to be regretted that this aim seems to have been more or less forgotten.

Without stretching the definition of condensation reactions, it can be added that ester formation with amides, carboxylic acids and acyl chlorides has been catalyzed by acceptor molecules (1937: 10; 1962: 19).

### d) Group transfer reactions

The Fries rearrangement reaction provides an example of acyl transfer. Thus the reaction $C_6H_4(CH_3)(OCOCH_3) \rightarrow CH_3CO{-}C_6H_3(OH)(CH_3)$ takes place employing $TiCl_4$ as catalyst (o-cresol is formed and $CO_2$ is eliminated in a parallel reaction). The yield is increased with mole ratios of $TiCl_4$ up to 2:1 (1956: 32). The net result of the reaction $C_6H_5NHCOCH_3$

$\rightarrow NH_2C_6H_4COCH_3$ is also an acyl transfer. The reaction is favoured by molecular amounts of $AlCl_3$ (1949: 9), $ZnCl_2$ and $SnCl_4$ (1952: 3).

Alkyl groups can also be transferred. Accordingly, it is thought that the addition of propylene to salicylic acid proceeds via the isopropyl-salicylate, which is rearranged so that the propyl group is transferred to the benzene nucleus, all in the presence of $BF_3$ (1934: 9).

The function of the catalyst in these rearrangements is far from clear.

## 26. A theory for donor-acceptor interaction with oxo-compounds

The aim of present-day fundamental research in chemistry is to progress beyond the mere description of chemical reactions. These efforts are seriously hampered for lack of a theory which would permit a quantitative discussion of the chemical bond. Although some quantitative theories appear to be available they are no more than empirical or at best semi-empirical rationalizations couched in a jargon which hides our actual ignorance. Accordingly, the word "theory" as it is used in this section of the book implies no more than an attempt to rationalize the preceding experimental facts. This is expressed in terms of some simple concepts which in a future, *truly* theoretical treatment should be reformulated on a firmer basis without loss of the overall picture obtained from the empirical rationalization. Owing to the lack of solid theoretical foundation, however, some of the proposed relationships might eventually prove to be fortuitous and without theoretical support.

### a) The nature of the donor-acceptor bond

An attempt will first be made to state clearly in which respects the donor-acceptor bond differs from other chemical bonds. We will take as a starting point the free atoms in the gas phase. The electronic structures of these atoms give a fairly good idea as to the probable valencies for different atomic species in different types of combination. It is true that if many *d* electrons are involved the predictions are more complicated, but even so it is possible to relate the common valencies of the atoms to electronic properties such as ionization energies in a straightforward way. The stoichiometric composition of a compound is determined by the *number of formal bonds* resulting from these valencies, which were described by WERNER as the principal valencies. In most compounds which do not contain bonds between identical atoms, these principal valencies coincide with what are today called oxidation or valence numbers. When WERNER became aware that in a molecular coordination compound or a salt, the existing bonds could not be identified directly with the principal valencies, he introduced the concept of auxiliary bonds. These are the additional bonds required to explain the coordination actually found in a given compound, and were supposed to originate in the "rest affinities" of the reacting species. Today, it is neither necessary nor useful to work with these concepts since we know that the principal and auxiliary valencies are often identical in nature. However, these concepts did permit a clear division of chemical reactions into those in which the principal valencies are changed and those in which only the coordinations are changed (Berzelius made a similar classification, expressed in still cruder terms). Donor-acceptor reactions obviously belong to the latter class, but the above definition also includes other types of reaction. Thus there are a great number of double decomposition reactions in which the main valencies are not changed but the bonds are rearranged. If further restrictions are imposed so that only those reactions are considered in which the original bonds remain unbroken although new bonds are formed, the instance of salt adduct formation is also eliminated, (compare the formal discussion p. 2) while some cases of double salt formation continue to resemble the formation of molecular adducts. The real difference here is that the latter comprise discrete units, the adduct molecules, while the double salts generally have infinite structures in two or three dimensions.

In view of the above comments, donor-acceptor interaction will be defined as *the interaction between donor and acceptor molecules leading to the formation of an adduct molecule which exhibits an increased coordination and an associated gain in energy.*

Starting from the free atoms, the energy of adduct formation will be greater than the sum of the energies of formation of the components. Accordingly, the donor and acceptor molecules may be regarded as possessing some "rest affinity" which is responsible for adduct formation. The conditions for the operation of "rest affinity" are selective, however, and a discussion of the donor-acceptor interaction must consider the selective conditions which are necessary for the formation of an adduct molecule. Analogous selective conditions are valid for double decomposition reactions, double salt formation or salt adduct formation, and it is because in all these cases the conditions differ to some degree that the present treatment has been restricted to molecular adducts. Most of the concepts can, however, be applied directly to salt-adduct formation.

The next step is to identify the "rest affinity" of donor and acceptor molecules. For a donor molecule it corresponds to the lone electron pairs which are available for bond formation with an acceptor. For an acceptor molecule it corresponds to the possibility of an increase or at least an improvement in coordination, the latter coming from a reduction in the number of shared bonds.

The only difference between this and other types of electron pair bond is that in adduct formation, the two electrons originate from a single atom, the donor atom. This does not alter the theoretical treatment of the bond.

In the valence-bond treatment the following electron distribution structures must be considered: D—A (both electrons located on the donor atom), $D^+$—$A^-$ (the electrons shared equally) and $D^{++}$—$A^{--}$ (both electrons located on the acceptor atom). All signs refer to formal charges. In cases of weak interaction the first structure must dominate, while with stronger interactions the importance of the other two structures increases. In terms of the molecular orbital $a\psi(D)+b\psi(A)$, the ratio of the coefficients $a:b$ will range from high to very low values with increasing interaction.

Although donor-acceptor bonds and other electron pair bonds are similar in character, there is one major difference between *compounds* containing donor-acceptor bonds and other compounds, namely that in the adduct the *total number of electrons involved in chemical bond formation is greater*. The result is a withdrawal of electron density from the donor atom and an increase in the electron density about the acceptor atom. The effect of this difference on the various bonds in a compound containing donor-acceptor bonds will be considered by comparison with the corresponding bonds in a compound from which donor-acceptor interactions are absent.

Further comment in connection with the very weak interaction is necessary since in a simple electrostatic sense, it is evident that dipole-dipole interactions might play a comparatively greater role if the electron pair donor-acceptor bond is very weak. It is well known that the dipole moment of the donor molecule is not a direct measure of the donor strength, even though dipole moment and donor strength often run parallel in very similar donor compounds. An electrostatic dipole-dipole interaction must exist, however, between the acceptor molecule (with its structure changed by adduct formation) and the donor molecule, and it is necessary to determine the extent to which such interactions can affect considerations of relative donor strengths.

Consideration of dipole-dipole interactions is necessary for two reasons. One is the possible weakness of the donor-acceptor interaction already mentioned; the other is the possibility of a high partial dipole moment for the acceptor molecule in the adduct. The more polar the bonds in the acceptor molecule, the smaller the probability that the simple predictions based on electron density considerations will be valid. This complication will be discussed later (p. 105); it does not influence the effects of outer substitution but it might be of importance when different types of donors and acceptors are compared.

### b) Factors determining the length of a given bond

The factors which might influence the length of a chemical bond formed between two atoms A and B with different environments are now discussed in general terms, and the results are used in the subsequent treatment of donor-acceptor interaction.

**Bond order and heteropolarity.** The most important factor determining the length of a bond seems to be the bond order, where this is rather loosely defined as the product of the coefficients $a$ and $b$ of the molecular orbital, $a\psi(A)+b\psi(B)$ (after appropriate normalizations), which is used to describe the bond. This concept of bond order has been used extensively in the discussion of $\pi$-bond orders, and in this case it has generally been assumed that the $\sigma$-bonds invariably have a bond order of unity ($a=b$). However, variation in the $\sigma$-bond order might be of major importance, and the discussion will begin with a consideration of the factors capable of influencing both $\sigma$- and $\pi$-bond orders.

From the definition of bond order it follows that it has its highest value if the electron pair is shared equally between the two atoms. The following rule can thus be formulated: *The greater the heteropolarity of a bond, the lower is its bond order.* The validity of this statement is self evident, and it is interesting to note that the bond orders defined in this way are also in fair agreement with the bond lengths, so long as the atoms A and B in the compounds under comparison have fairly similar environments. This is basically an empirical rule, which at best can only be made plausible by theoretical considerations (1962: 23). However, a summary of the present knowledge of bond length variations shows that the heteropolarity variation is the most important single factor influencing polar single bonds (1960: 63), and the discussion will be based on the rule that *a higher heteropolarity gives a weaker bond, as is manifested in the bond lengths of polar bonds*. This applies to both $\sigma$- and isolated $\pi$-bonds.

**Hybridization.** Where the bonds are non-polar or have a very low heteropolarity, some other factor is probably more important. It is obvious that heteropolarity must be less important under these circumstances, since the bond order alters little with changes in $a:b$ if $a \sim b$. It has been pointed out by many different authors that in such cases variations in hybridization must be taken into account in the discussion of $\sigma$-bonds. The greater the $s$ character of a hybrid orbital, the shorter is its bond radius. (The evidence is reviewed by Bent (1961: 50).) Bent formulated the purely empirical relation: *The s character of bonds tends to be concentrated in those orbitals of an atom which are used for interaction with electropositive substituents.* The $s$-character is determined from the bond angles, the occurrence of orthogonal hybridization being assumed.

It is seen that both heteropolarity and hybridization are influenced by the electronegativities of the groups bonded to the atoms A and B.

These influences will be designated *electronegativity effects.* In most instances it will be observed that the two factors influence bond lengths in the same sense, and while it might easily be supposed that they are identical this is not the case. The difference is the same as that between bond polarity induced by the partial transfer of electron density (heteropolarity) and that induced by the partial use of $p$-orbitals (hybridization). If $CF_4$ and $CCl_4$ are considered as examples it is clear that the heteropolarity of the C—F bond is much greater than that of the C—Cl bond, whereas the hybridization is the same, namely $sp^3$. As has been shown, heteropolarity is of greatest interest in connection with polar bonds and hybridization in connection with non-polar bonds.

**Delocalization.** If $\pi$-bonds are not isolated and if they have the same symmetry, an extended delocalization of $\pi$-electrons can occur. The $\pi$-bond order might thus change as a result of variations in delocalization, and this effect could be decisive in determining the $\pi$-bond order. From a theoretical point of view it has been easier to consider the delocalization of $\pi$-bonds than to discuss $\sigma$-bonds, and the molecular orbital approach permits of many predictions on this basis. If such predictions are to be made it is necessary to consider the effect on the bond lengths of variations in the $\pi$-bond order. Because of the greater mobility of the $\pi$-electrons the effect is often appreciable. This influence will be designated the *delocalization effect*.

The brief and schematic treatment of bond length variations given above will be elaborated by subsequent discussion of specific cases.

**The donor-acceptor bond.** The discussion now returns to the differences between donor-acceptor bonds and normal valence bonds. It was concluded (p. 88) that in compounds experiencing donor-acceptor interactions, the donor atoms have a lower and the acceptor atoms a higher electron density than the atoms in compounds from which such interactions are absent. It follows that, by comparison with atoms in non-adduct compounds, the electron affinity is greater for an atom acting as a donor and lower for an atom acting as an acceptor. If the donor atom is more electronegative than the acceptor, as is usually the case in coordination chemistry, the heteropolarity of the donor-acceptor bond will be higher. The bond will therefore be weaker than bonds in compounds lacking donor-acceptor interactions. However, all the other bonds in the adduct will be influenced in a similar way (to be considered later) although to a smaller extent. There is therefore no essential difference between donor-acceptor and other bonds, but there *is* a difference between compounds containing donor-acceptor bonds and those from which such bonds are absent.

### c) The nature of the oxo-bond

Discussion of the nature of the oxo-bonds in oxo-compounds has been very extensive, but often rather confused. One of the reasons for this confusion is the unqualified use of the terms single and double bonds. Thus the "double" bonds $C=O$ and $S=O$ are very different in character, and this fact must be taken into consideration in all comparisons of compounds containing such groups.

**The $>C=O$ bond.** The $>C=O$ bond constitutes the simplest case and will therefore be considered first. It is firmly established that the carbon atom in this bond has a planar, trigonal coordination; in terms of hybrid orbitals, three $\sigma$-bonds are formed by $sp^2$ hybridization. The remaining $p$-orbital, together with a $p$-orbital from the oxygen atom, generates the $\pi$-bond. One might ask whether a better description might not be given in terms of the semipolar bond $>C^+—O^-$. Owing to the charges present such a bond would be less heteropolar than a normal single bond and therefore stronger. However, PAULING gave the answer to this question in his classical treatment of polar bonds which leads to the conclusion that the partial dipole moment for the electron distribution in $>C^+—O^-$ would be much larger than that actually found (even assuming the single bond to be nonpolar).

The rules developed in the preceding chapter are valid for both the $\sigma$-bonds and the $\pi$-bond. The introduction of a more electronegative substitutent at the carbon atom will thus decrease the heteropolarity of the C=O $\sigma$- and $\pi$-bonds, and the bond will therefore be stronger and shorter. This effect is clearly demonstrated from a comparison of $(CH_3)_2CO$ and $COCl_2$, in which the C=O bond lengths are 1.22 and 1.17 Å, respectively. The results of many other studies also indicate the occurrence of this effect, although it diminishes as the substitution occurs at an increasing distance from the C=O bond or if the difference in electronegativity is less marked.

With carboxylic acids, esters, lactones and amides the conditions are very different. These compounds contain oxygen and nitrogen atoms adjacent to the carbon atom of the C=O bond. These atoms have lone pairs of electrons which can be delocalized in molecular $\pi$-orbitals extending over the whole group O, C, O or O, C, N. Since the contributory $p$-orbitals from the three atoms must be at least roughly parallel, they *and* the other atoms bonded to them must be coplanar, as shown below. The planarity of the amides has been demonstrated in a series of structure determinations (reviewed recently (1957: 33)), but the evidence is less complete for the other types of compound. However, the structural conditions for delocalization of a lone pair of electrons on the oxygen or nitrogen atoms seem to be fulfilled and the next step is to examine the effect of delocalization on the bond lengths. (It should be observed that two papers have appeared recently which claim that no delocalization occurs in carboxylic acids and esters (1958: 43; 1961: 51). As will be seen in a later chapter (p. 103) the relative donor properties of ketones and esters cannot be understood on the basis of such an assumption.) The delocalization can be expressed by means of the following electron distribution structures:

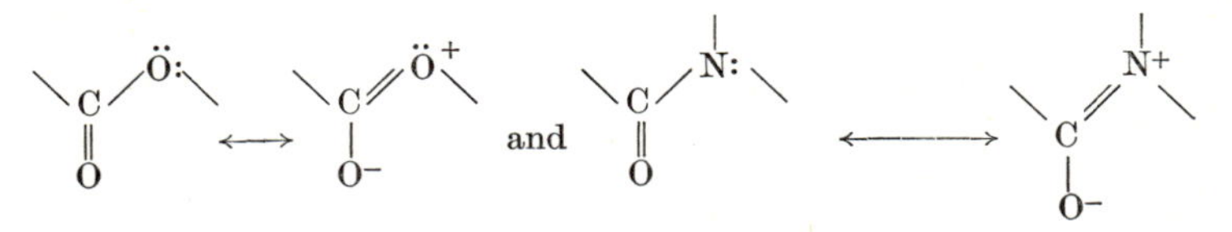


On comparing the C=O bond in an ester with that in a ketone it is found that the introduction of an alkoxy group has two effects. The higher electronegativity of the group should lead to a reduced heteropolarity and a stronger bond (the "electronegativity effect"). On the other hand the delocalization of the lone pair of electrons which results should obviously decrease the $\pi$-bond order and make the bond weaker (the "delocalization effect"). In general the C=O bond lengths in ketones and esters are very similar, indicating that the two effects almost cancel each other.

On comparing the C—O bond in an ether and in an ester, three main effects can be considered as contributing to a relative shortening of this bond in the ester. Thus in the ester the valence state of the carbon atom changes from $sp^3$ to $sp^2$ hybridization. The adjacent C=O bond in the ester attracts more electrons from the carbon atom, thus leading to a decrease in the heteropolarity of the C—O bond as compared with the ether (the "electronegativity effect"). Finally, delocalization increases the $\pi$ bond order. This last may be the principal effect, but it is not the only one as is generally assumed. The average C—O bond length in carboxylic acids and esters is actually 1.36 Å compared with 1.43 Å in alcohols and ethers. Similar effects are observed in amides, and it will be shown later that the relative donor strengths of these molecules give clear support to the view that they contain molecular orbitals which extend over the three-atom groups.

One other observation can be made at this point, namely that the existence of compounds containing the C=O bond is a result of the favourable energy condition of the C=O bond, although polymerization with the alternative formation of two single bonds is possible under certain conditions (the formation of paraformaldehyde is one example). By contrast, the configuration with the higher coordination always results in the corresponding RBO and $R_2SiO$ compounds and leads to polymerization through the formation of B—O—B and Si—O—Si bonds. Although it could not have been predicted, this difference in behaviour is understandable. Thus it is to be expected that the Si=O bond would be weaker than the C=O bond, an effect which arises from the general difference between the first two rows in the periodic system. In the boron compounds, on the other hand, a B=O bond would lead to a very low coordination, a condition which is energetically unfavourable.

**Other oxo-bonds.** A different situation arises in connection with $\sigma$- and $\pi$-bonding in the groups S=O, Se=O, P=O and As=O. In the donor molecules including these groups, quoted in this book, the $\sigma$-bonds correspond roughly to $sp^3$ hybridization (in some cases with lone electron pairs). Accordingly there are no $s$ or $p$ electrons available in S, Se, P or As for the formation of a $\pi$ bond with a $p$-orbital of the donor oxygen atom. The octet rule can also be quoted as opposing double bond formation. $d$-orbitals are available, however, and a very plausible argument has been advanced for their use in $\pi$-bond formation (1950: 7; 1954: 20; 1961: 52). The controversy regarding semipolar bond versus double bond formation in these groups has followed much the same lines as that about the C=O bond, but the conclusions are less unanimous. Dipole moment studies have been advanced in support of double bond formation (1945: 8; 1956: 33) but values for molar refractivity have been used as evidence for semipolar bonds (1958: 44 with many references) while the solvent effects on UV spectra have also been discussed (1958: 45). Unfortunately, the supporters of both arguments have been led to introduce many assumptions to prove their points, and it would be difficult to say that one view is wholly correct and the other wrong. (Similar views have been expressed by other authors (1956: 34; 1960: 47).) In this discussion it will first be assumed that double bonds exist, and the effects of this assumption will be explored by considering aspects of the character of such bonds.

The main difference between these bonds and the C=O bond has already been stated, namely that the molecular $\pi$-orbital is here formed by one or more $d$-orbitals of the phosphorus atom (for example) and a $p$-orbital of the oxygen atom (or $p$-orbitals of more than one oxygen atom). However, the electron affinity of a $d$-orbital is appreciably lower than that of an $sp^3$ hybrid orbital. It follows that the heteropolarity of the $\pi$-bond will be much higher than that of the $\sigma$-bond. For the purpose of this discussion it is immaterial whether or not the actual electron distribution represents an equalization of the difference in heteropolarity; the main point is that the extra bond strength due to the $\pi$-bond is much less in such a group than in the C = O bond, even on a relative scale.

The difference between double bond and semipolar bond formation will therefore be much smaller for S = O, Se = O, P = O and As = O bonds than for the C = O bond. Bearing this in mind, the two controversial ideas mentioned above need not be considered too closely, since both are over-simplifications of the problem. It will be found that the picture given here is of assistance in understanding the information at present available regarding the role of these compounds as donor molecules.

Further discussion of this point will be given later. At this stage consideration is limited, as in the case of the C = O bond, to some of the effects on bond lengths produced by substitution within the donor molecules. The effects are clearly seen in comparisons of $SOF_2$ and $(CH_3)_2SO$, and of $SO_2F_2$ and $(CH_3)_2SO_2$. The greater electronegativity of the fluorine atom leads to a lower polarity in the S = O bonds and also to a higher $s$-character, both effects contributing to a decrease in bond length. Values for the S = O bond in these four compounds are 1.41 and 1.47 Å, and 1.37 and 1.44 Å, respectively (1960: 63). Another representative example is the variation of the P = O bond stretching frequency in different phosphoryl compounds (1954: 21). This is a smooth variation which depends upon the electronegativities of other groups bonded to the phosphorus atom; thus the strength of the P = O bond increases with increasing electronegativity of the substitutent. Direct bond length determinations of $POCl_3$ and $(CH_3)_3PO$ indicate the same effect; the P = O bond lengths are 1.45 Å and 1.48 Å (1960: 63).

It is noteworthy that amides and esters containing this type of double bond also seem to conform quite well with the electronegativity order (1954: 21) and the delocalization effect must therefore be comparatively weak, if it is present at all. (Compare also the later discussion of donor strengths, p. 102.)

Finally, the comparison of compounds containing one and two S = O bonds is very instructive. Comparing $SOF_2$ and $SO_2F_2$ the following effects can be predicted: the introduction of a second S = O bond will decrease the heteropolarity of the other bonds and thus strengthen them; the $s$-character of the other bonds from the sulfur atom will increase leading to an increase in the F—S—F bond angle and to a stronger S—F bond. On passing from $SOF_2$ to $SO_2F_2$ the S—F bond length actually decreases from 1.585 Å to 1.503 Å, and the S = O bond length from 1.412 Å to 1.405 Å, while the F—S—F bond angle increases from $92^{0}49'$ to $96^{0}7'$ (1961: 50). Similar effects are observed on passing from $PX_3$ to $POX_3$ (1961: 50). On the other hand, on passing from $(CH_3)_2SO$ to $(CH_3)_2SO_2$, the heteropolarity of the C—S bond *increases* since in this instance the direction of the original polarity is different from that in the earlier example. (In this connection it should be remembered that the presence of a single S=O bond in $(CH_3)_2SO$ is sufficient to increase the polarity of the C—S bond by comparison with that in a thioether, since the effective electronegativity of the sulfur atom is enhanced owing to electron withdrawal by the oxygen atom.) The increased heteropolarity in the sulfone will result in a weakening and lengthening of the C—S bond. Observed values are 1.82 Å for the sulfoxide and 1.90 Å for the sulfone. Since hybridization should have an opposing effect (compare above) it is obvious that the C—S bond in the sulfoxide is sufficiently polar to make the heteropolarity shift the most important factor.

It is significant that two opposing effects can be predicted by this treatment as compared with other theoretical interpretations, which generally consider only one of the two possibilities (1960: 63).

### d) Donor-acceptor interaction. Influence on the donor molecule

Consideration of the donor-acceptor interaction in oxo-compounds will begin with a discussion of its influence on donor molecules. This discussion will be based on the description of the bonds in oxo-compounds given in the preceding chapter and on the assumption that the main effect of donor-acceptor interaction is an electron density withdrawal from the donor oxygen atom.

**Bond lengths.** In instances where the oxo-bonds (both $\sigma$- and $\pi$-bonds) are isolated, the initial result of electron density withdrawal should be an increase in bond heteropolarity leading to a decrease in bond strength. There should be a simultaneous increase in the *s*-character of the hybrid orbital used by the oxygen atom in oxo-bond formation. This is another application of the empirical rule formulated earlier, that the *s*-character of bonds tends to become concentrated in those orbitals which the atom uses for interaction with electropositive substituents. The electron withdrawal to the new donor-acceptor bond enhances the relative electropositive character of the other atom bonded to oxygen. The increased *s*-character should make the oxo-bond shorter. Most oxo-bonds are highly polar, however, and the heteropolarity shift can therefore be expected to constitute the most important effect, a weakening (and lengthening) of the bond being obtained. Evidence for the weakening of oxo-bonds is afforded by a considerable number of examples described in the experimental results of various structure studies, mainly spectroscopic. (UV shifts towards longer wave lengths also give similar indications (1951:17).)

Consideration will next be given to the effect on adjacent bonds in instances where the oxo-bonds are isolated. Two effects will again be present, namely shifts of polarity and increased *s*-character of the hybrid orbital used in $\sigma$-bond formation. Three alternative cases result. In the first, the heteropolarity of the bond is reduced from its original level and the polarity and hybridization effects cooperate and lead to bond strengthening. This has been found to be the case for $POCl_3$ adducts, and it can safely be predicted for all donor molecules containing bonds to a halogen atom adjacent to the oxo-bond. In the second case, the bond is almost nonpolar and the hybridization effect dominates and leads at least to a small bond strengthening. This has been found to be the case for ketone adducts. Thirdly, the heteropolarity is increased beyond its original level and the two effects oppose each other. If the bond is not markedly polar it is difficult to predict which effect will dominate, but if the bond is appreciably polar a weakening can be expected. All the organo-metalloid oxides have bonds which do not exhibit marked polarity, and further investigations are needed to determine which of the two effects is most important for the different donors. Conflicting results have been reported for sulfoxide adducts (p. 73).

The effects on the donor molecules are too small to be confirmed with certainty by the structural studies, owing to a lack of sufficiently accurate information about the adduct or the free donor molecule.

The above picture is altered significantly in the presence of an appreciable delocalization effect, such as occurs in esters and amides. The withdrawal of electron density from the oxygen atom leads to a reduction of the $\sigma$- and $\pi$-bond orders in the oxo-bond in precisely the same way as in ketones. The same effect will also be felt by the adjacent bond but here there is also the possibility that the $\pi$-bond order will be increased. Bond strengthening should thus be more pronounced with esters and amides than with ketones. Too few detailed studies have been reported to permit further discussion, but the structure of the $HgCl_2$ adduct with coumarin indicates a marked change (p. 64). It now becomes clear that a consideration of *both* electronegativity and delocalization effects is necessary before a consistent discussion of all the information on esters and amides can be undertaken.

**Bond angles subtended at the donor atom.** At this point something must also be said about the bond angles subtended at the donor oxygen atom. This angle should depend mainly upon the distribution of the *s*-electrons. An increase in the *s*-character of the lone electron pair, and accordingly an increase in the *p*-character in the other two bonds, should lead to a smaller bond angle. According to the empirical rule due to BENT (p. 89) the *s*-character of the lone electron pair will increase with increasing electronegativity of the groups bonded to the oxygen. In Table 15 the bond angles in some adducts are compared with the sums of the electronegativities of the atoms bonded to oxygen. It is obvious from the table that other factors, particularly steric factors, must also be of importance. The bond angles in the arsine oxide adducts are smaller than in the $POCl_3$ and phosphine oxide adducts, although the arsenic atom is less electronegative than the phosphorous atom. The $As=O$ bond is appreciably longer than the $P=O$ bonds, however, and a lower bond angle is therefore sterically favoured. In the same way the two effects counteract each other in donors containing $S=O$ and $Se=O$ bonds and the adducts accordingly have very similar bond angles. These are smaller than for adducts of donors containing P = O and As = O bonds. This difference can also be interpreted in terms of steric factors, since the sulfoxides and $SeOCl_2$ are molecules in which the central atom has one open side which

Table 15. *Bond angles subtended at oxygen in a number of adducts*

| Adduct | Bond angle | Electronegativity sum |
|---|---|---|
| $(TiCl_4 \cdot POCl_3)_2$ | 151.8° | 3.7 |
| $NbCl_5 \cdot POCl_3$ | 148.8° | ? |
| $SbCl_3 \cdot 2(C_6H_5)_3AsO$ | 140.9° | 3.8 |
| | 137.2° | |
| $HgCl_2 \cdot 2(C_6H_5)_3AsO$ | 136.7° | ? |
| | 134.4° | |
| $SbCl_5 \cdot (CH_3)_3PO$ | 144.9° | 3.9 |
| $SbCl_5 \cdot POCl_3$ | 145.0° | 3.9 |
| $SnCl_4 \cdot 2SeOCl_2$ | 121.5° | 4.1 |
| $SnCl_4 \cdot 2(CH_3)_2SO$ | 121° | 4.2 |
| | 126° | |
| $SbCl_5 \cdot SeOCl_2$ | 120.9° | 4.2 |
| | 121.7° | |
| $SbCl_5 \cdot (C_6H_5)_2SO$ | 117° | 4.3 |
| $SbCl_5 \cdot (CH_3)_2SO_2$ | 138.7° | 4.3 |
| $BF_3 \cdot (CH_3)_2SO$ | 119.2° | 4.5 |

permits lower bond angles. It is noteworthy that the sulfone adduct (without any open side) has a much larger bond angle, which is of the same order as those in the adducts of $POCl_3$ and arsine oxide. The results of this discussion can be compared with the general observations given on p. 76 regarding bond angles about the acceptor atom.

## e) Differences between free bonds and bridging bonds

At this point it is necessary to distinguish between bridging bonds with and without donor-acceptor interaction. There are no difficulties in the latter case; it is easy to understand the difference between single and double bonds, as for example between the C—O—C bonds in an ether and the C = O bond in a ketone.

In the donor molecules under discussion, the free oxo-bond is changed in the adduct to a bridging bond by the formation of a *new bond*. It has been seen that this type of bridging also lowers the strength of the oxo-bond, to an extent depending upon the degree of the donor-acceptor interaction (electron density withdrawal) but not necessarily to the level of a single bond. Halogen bridges are of a similar character. A typical example is given by $AlCl_3$, which in the gas phase and in some solvents does not exist as a molecule with three free Al—Cl bonds, but rather as the $Al_2Cl_6$ dimer containing two Al—Cl—Al bridges. This can be regarded as formed by donor-acceptor interaction between two $AlCl_3$ molecules, aluminium being the acceptor atom and chlorine the donor atom. Consequently the electron density about aluminium is relatively higher, and that about chlorine relatively lower, than in compounds from which donor-acceptor interaction is absent. Accordingly, the bridging Al—Cl bonds should be longer than the free Al—Cl bonds, which are influenced by this bridge formation to a much smaller extent. The actual bond lengths are 2.06 Å and 2.21 Å respectively (1960: 63). Comparable differences are found in $Nb_2Cl_{10}$ and $Ta_2Cl_{10}$. The difference between free and bridging bonds is considerable, and it is possible that hybridization changes are also of importance. For the purposes of this discussion it is sufficient to remember that bridge formation is more important than any other single factor in determining the relative bond strengths within similar molecules. This effect is shown in the dimeric molecule $(TiCl_4 \cdot POCl_3)_2$ in which the short Ti—Cl bonds are 2.22 Å and the long Ti—Cl bonds are 2.49 Å (average values).

Another cause of the weakening of bridging bonds can be inferred from a theoretical study of oxo-bonds (1961: 52). According to this treatment both lone *p*-electron pairs could be used for $\pi$-bond formation in the free oxo-compound. This would correspond to *sp* hybridization of the oxygen orbitals. In the adduct, one of the lone pairs of electrons would be used for the donor-acceptor bond and only one *p* lone pair would then be available for $\pi$-bond formation, thus leading to a lower $\pi$-bond order. It is difficult to say if this is a reasonable suggestion in the absence of any discussion of the energies necessary for promotion to the hybridized *sp*-valence state. It is also difficult to see how an explanation of this kind can be advanced to account for the formation of halogen bridges.

## f) Donor-acceptor interaction. Influence on the acceptor molecule

In the formal discussion of the conditions for molecular adduct formation it was emphasized that the coordination of the acceptor atom is necessarily altered by adduct formation. Structural changes in the acceptor molecule are therefore more pronounced than those in the donor molecule. An attempt at this point to consider the various acceptor atoms in a systematic manner would be largely a repetition of the structural facts presented in the chapter on typical coordination numbers. Too little is known of the fundamental background to permit a really theoretical discussion in most cases.

**Acceptor molecules.** Considering acceptor molecules first, it is easily possible to *describe* the facts in words which give the impression of a theoretical treatment. However, the consider gains little from the statement that the hybridization changes from $sp^2$ to $sp^3$ on passing from trigonal to tetrahedral coordination, from $sp^3$ to $sp^3d^2$ or $d^2sp^3$ on passing from tetrahedral to octahedral coordination, and from $sp^3d$ to $sp^3d^2$ on passing from a trigonal bipyramid to an octahedron. This states simply that the theory is sufficiently developed to account for the occurrence of the alternative conditions. Greater value would attach to predictions regarding the relative stabilities of these configurations, i. e. the energy changes which are experienced on passing from one coordination to another.

A treatment of this kind for $BX_3$ and $AlX_3$ acceptor molecules has been attempted by Cotton and Leto (1959: 59) and their results will be

examined briefly, using $BF_3$ as an example. The empty $p$-orbital of the boron atom permits delocalization of the lone pairs on the fluorine atoms and this gives rise to electron distribution structures of the form $F{=}B\langle^{F}_{F}$.
COTTON and LETO have calculated the overlap integrals for this $\pi$-bond interaction in the compounds $BX_3$ where X = F, Cl and Br, and have also estimated the relative $\pi$-bond energies. These energies are lost when adducts are formed by means of $sp^3$ hybrid bonds. The calculations show that this loss is greatest for $BF_3$ and diminishes in the order $BF_3 > BCl_3 > BBr_3$. This would explain the surprising order of acceptor strengths found on comparing these compounds. (See also p. 108.) The energy change associated with the rehybridization from $sp^2$ to $sp^3$ orbitals has been estimated from the relative overlap integrals for the $\sigma$-bonds and has been found to be very small and in fact negligible compared with the loss of $\pi$-bond energy. While the arbitrariness involved in these conclusions is evident, they do suggest that in this case the rearrangement energy is not very important. On the other hand the use of $sp^3$ instead of $sp^2$ orbitals and the greater heteropolarity of these bonds compared with those of the free acceptor molecule should lead to weaker B—X bonds in the adducts, even though no $\pi$-bond energy were lost. The resulting changes in bond length are appreciable, in agreement with the view that many factors cooperate. In this way the B—F bond length in $BF_3$ is increased from 1.30 Å to 1.39 Å in the adduct with $(CH_3)_2NH$.

Smaller effects might be expected in changes from tetrahedral to octahedral coordination, but they should still be obvious. Many examples are known and it is sufficient here to mention the large increase in the Sn—Cl bond length from 2.31 Å in $SnCl_4$ to 2.38 Å (average value) in the 1:2 adduct with $SeOCl_2$. (Similar conclusions have been reached from RAMAN spectra studies (1962: 28).)

A less certain case is the development of octahedral coordination from an acceptor molecule with trigonal bipyramidal coordination. The latter structure seems to be relatively unfavourable and the bonds are unsymmetrical. This makes the comparison less direct but the average Sb—Cl bond length in $SbCl_5$ is 2.36 Å and similar or lower values are found in most 1:1 adducts of $SbCl_5$. The difficulty to discuss trigonal bipyramidal coordination is obvious if we consider the structure of $SbCl_3 \cdot 2(C_6H_5)_3AsO$ which contains *two* distinctly different types of Sb—Cl bond length (p. 70).

**Acceptors with infinite structures.** With *monomeric acceptor molecules* an increase of coordination always occurs as a result of donor-acceptor interaction. If the acceptor compounds contain *infinite or finite halogen bridges*, there is generally no increase of coordination number, while in some cases even a change to a *lower* coordination occurs. A substantial *improvement in coordination* can still be achieved since there will be some reduction in the sharing of halogen atoms with other acceptor atoms. The simplest case of unchanged coordination is the formation of $AlCl_3 \cdot D$ adduct molecules in the gas phase or in suitable solvents. The coordination of aluminium is tetrahedral both in $Al_2Cl_6$ and in the adduct. In the adduct, however, halogen atoms are no longer shared and the resulting improvement in coordination makes adduct formation energetically possible although two Al—Cl bonds must first be broken.

Two other cases of unchanged coordination number are well demonstrated by the two acceptor compounds $CdCl_2$ and $ZnCl_2$. Both have infinite structures, based upon octahedral coordination in $CdCl_2$ and tetrahedral coordination in $ZnCl_2$, and both form 1:2 adducts. The $ZnCl_2$ adducts are molecular and in those which have been studied, the Zn—Cl bond length ranges from 2.24 Å to 2.30 Å, compared with the values 2.26 Å to 2.34 Å found in the three different modifications of $ZnCl_2$ (1959: 60). The difference, although small, is in the expected direction. In $CdCl_2$ the chlorine atoms bridge *three* different acceptor atoms; accordingly, the formation of a 1:2 adduct leads, to some extent, to the break-up of these halogen bridges. Thus, at each chlorine atom, one bond is broken so that only two acceptor atoms are bridged. There are then two ligand sites available for the donor molecules. This is the structure of most $CdCl_2 \cdot 2D$ adducts (Fig. 3). The relative bond lengths should be determined mainly by the extent to which the sharing of halogen atoms occurs; thus the Cd—Cl bond lengths in bis-biuret-cadmium chloride are only 2.55–2.62 Å (1960: 7) compared with 2.74 Å in $CdCl_2$.

Reduction of coordination number is exemplified by some $CoCl_2$ adducts. As mentioned earlier (p. 9) there are examples of adduct molecules $CoCl_2 \cdot 2D$ in which the configuration is tetrahedral, whereas $CoCl_2$ has a layer lattice with octahedral coordination. In other adducts the octahedral coordination is preserved and structures of the same type as the $CdCl_2 \cdot 2D$ adducts are obtained (e. g. in $CoCl_2 \cdot 2C_5H_5N$). In the latter compound the Co—Cl bond length is 2.49 Å compared with 2.26–2.34 Å in the molecular adducts with tetrahedral coordination. (The bond length in $CoCl_2$ is not firmly established.)

**Comparison between the effects of different donors.** It has been assumed that the formation of an adduct leads to an increase in the electron density about the acceptor atom, thus causing an increase in the heteropolarity of the remaining bonds to the acceptor atom. These bonds will therefore be weakened to a degree which depends upon the transfer of electron density to the acceptor atom. Accurate structure determinations are needed for comparisons of this type, and there should be appreciable differences between the donors which are compared. A possible comparison is that between $Cl^-$ ions and neutral molecules containing oxygen or nitrogen as donor atoms (1960: 63). The electron density about the acceptor atom should be increased much more by the $Cl^-$ ion than by the neutral molecules and the remaining bonds in the negatively charged complex should accordingly be weaker than those in the adduct molecules. Some obvious differences are as follows: Sb—Cl is 2.47 Å in $SbCl_6^-$ but only 2.32–2.35 Å in a number of 1:1 adducts with neutral molecules; Ti—Cl is 2.33–2.35 Å in $TiCl_6^{2-}$ but only 2.20–2.24 Å in a 1:1 adduct (free bonds); Co—Cl is 2.34 Å in $CoCl_4^{2-}$ but only 2.26 Å in a molecular adduct (1957: 2). This type of effect has generally been neglected in discussions of successive complex formation in aqueous solution, where it must also be of some importance.

**Comparison of the tin and titanium tetrachlorides as acceptor molecules.** It is noteworthy that $TiCl_4$ (and $ZrCl_4$ and $HfCl_4$) forms 1:1 and 1:2 adducts while $SnCl_4$ forms 1:2 adducts almost exclusively. This prompts the question: What is the reason for this difference and why does $TiCl_4$ form halogen bridges in 1:1 adducts but not in the free acceptor molecule?

At present the only clue to the first part of the question is probably the fact that the Ti—Cl bond is much more polar than the Sn—Cl bond (see p. 80). If the bond were completely ionic bridge, formation would be favoured by the high electron density about the chlorine atom and the absence of structural restrictions on bond formation from this atom. However, this explanation is only satisfactory if a reasonable answer has also been given to the second part of the question. For this purpose it is convenient to consider the hypothetical monomeric molecule $TiCl_4 \cdot POCl_3$ which might very well exist in solution in different solvents. The addition of a donor molecule to $TiCl_4$ will increase the electron density about the titanium atom and the Ti—Cl bond will accordingly become more heteropolar, and the formation of halogen bridges will be favoured, as explained above. Thus a consistent explanation for the whole problem seems possible. In this connection, the accurate determination of more $TiCl_4 \cdot D$ adduct structures would be of value in providing evidence for the occurrence of halogen bridge formation in such adducts.

Halogen-bridge formation should be most easily effected by strongly polar bonds since these provide the highest electron density about the chlorine atoms. However, as a result of bridge formation the electron density about the bridging chlorine atoms would be greatly reduced and in consequence it should be lower than that about the chlorine atoms in the free bonds. It should be possible to check this prediction by NMR studies.

## g) The strength of donor-acceptor interaction

**Effect of outer substitution. Bond lengths.** The general problem of the strength of donor-acceptor interaction will be dealt with in stages. The first step is to consider the effect of substitution occurring at the atom adjacent to the donor oxygen, an effect denoted by the term "outer substitution". Of the factors determining the bond strength, bond heteropolarity is, as before, the most important. The bond system connecting the acceptor atom, the donor oxygen, and its nearest atomic neighbour in the donor molecule is unchanged by substitution and it remains only to consider the effect of the substitution on the last of these atoms. Unfortunately very few structure determinations are available which permit comparisons but one obvious case is provided by the difference between the Sb—O bond in $SbCl_5 \cdot POCl_3$ and in $SbCl_5 \cdot (CH_3)_3PO$. The bond system $Cl_5Sb—O=P\lt$ is common to the two adducts and substitution of Cl for $CH_3$ should lead to a lower electron density about the phosphorus atom, inducing also, as a secondary effect, a lower electron density about the oxygen atom. Thus the heteropolarity of the Sb—O bond and therefore also the bond length will increase. The actual Sb—O distances in the two compounds are 1.99 Å and 2.12 Å, respectively. The magnitude of the effect indicates an appreciable mobility for the $\pi$-bond electrons of the P=O bond and this conclusion is also borne out by the marked reduction in its length from 1.61 Å to 1.46 Å. The polarity of the P=O bond should decrease, but the magnitude of the effect is higher than that which would be expected for a $\sigma$-bond. (Many examples of $\sigma$-bond effects have been given in a recent paper (1960: 63).) Thus the effect of substitution within a molecule, as considered earlier in the discussion of bond length variations, is the same in this more complicated case of a compound containing donor-acceptor bonds, if both $\sigma$- and $\pi$-bonds are considered.

**Bond length differences.** Consideration of the structures of oxide halide adducts shows clearly that the bond lengths cannot be described easily in terms of ideal ionic or covalent radii (1960: 65). The first point to note is that while the formation of "ideal single bonds" cannot be predicted with certainty, the *difference in length* between the bonds to oxygen and to chlorine should be independent of the individual compound. The values of some such differences are given in Table 16.

Table 16. *Differences between bond lengths to chlorine and to oxygen in some adducts*

| | | |
|---|---|---|
| $SbCl_5 \cdot POCl_3$ | $\lvert P—Cl \rvert — \lvert P—O \rvert = 0.48$ Å | $\lvert Sb—Cl \rvert — \lvert Sb—O \rvert = 0.16$ Å |
| $NbCl_5 \cdot POCl_3$ | $\lvert P—Cl \rvert — \lvert P—O \rvert = 0.49$ Å | $\lvert Nb—Cl \rvert — \lvert Nb—O \rvert = 0.14$ Å |
| $SnCl_4 \cdot 2POCl_3$ | $\lvert P—Cl \rvert — \lvert P—O \rvert = 0.48$ Å | $\lvert Sn—Cl \rvert — \lvert Sn—O \rvert = 0.06$ Å |
| $(TiCl_4 \cdot POCl_3)_2$ | $\lvert P—Cl \rvert — \lvert P—O \rvert = 0.52$ Å | $\lvert Ti—Cl \rvert — \lvert Ti—O \rvert = 0.12$ Å |
| $SnCl_4 \cdot 2SeOCl_2$ | $\lvert Se—Cl \rvert — \lvert Se—O \rvert = 0.41$ Å | $\lvert Sn—Cl \rvert — \lvert Sn—O \rvert = 0.26$ Å |
| $SbCl_5 \cdot SeOCl_2$ | $\lvert Se—Cl \rvert — \lvert Se—O \rvert = 0.43$ Å | $\lvert Sb—Cl \rvert — \lvert Sb—O \rvert = 0.25$ Å |

The difference between the adducts of $POCl_3$ and those of $SeOCl_2$ is obvious. (The deviation for $SnCl_4 \cdot 2POCl_3$ is well within the limits of experimental error, which are rather large for this compound.)

The difference |P—Cl|—|P—O| is definitely larger than the corresponding difference |Se—Cl|—|Se—O| and the bond length differences on the acceptor side show the opposite trend. It is of interest to compare these differences with values expected in the absence of donor-acceptor interaction in a compound containing ideal single bonds. In the paper referred to it is concluded that a bond length difference of 0.32 Å would be a reasonable value. It is easily seen that, within the limits of accuracy, the deviations from this value for the donor and acceptor components of the adduct are of the same magnitude but of opposite sign.

Clearly, the $SeOCl_2$ adducts contain a bond system showing a smaller departure from the single bond model, i. e. Se—O—Acceptor, than does the bond system in the $POCl_3$ adducts where the P=O double bond character is more pronounced. It is also seen that the donor molecule exhibits an increasing departure from a double bond model with increasing strength of the new bond. This approach, of considering bond length differences, offers an alternative view of the factors which determine the effects of donor-acceptor interaction on the bonds in both donor and acceptor molecules.

The other adducts whose structures have been studied also exhibit departures from ideal bond length differences, but simple relationships of the kind described for the oxide-halide adducts have not been found. (This was in fact predicted in the reference given above.)

**Thermochemical studies.** Enthalpy measurements provide an alternative means of estimating the strength of the donor-acceptor interaction. In this connection, it is first necessary to see whether the heat of reaction for $D(g)+A(g)=DA(g)$ can yield relevant information and for this purpose the different steps in the reaction are considered.

The measured change of enthalpy is the sum of many different partial effects; since both donor and acceptor molecules are influenced by the interaction it becomes difficult to predict how the various positive and negative terms will balance each other. However, adduct formation is an exothermic reaction in all instances. Accordingly, it seems reasonable to assume that the effects of adduct formation on the donor and acceptor molecules will be roughly proportional to the strength of the interaction between the donor and the acceptor atoms, at least so long as only outer substitution is considered. The heats of reaction will then be proportional to the strength of the interaction even if they do not give the absolute values of the donor-acceptor bond energies, if such bond energies can ever be satisfactorily defined. The value of the interpretation is reduced since, for the majority of cases, the reactions cannot be studied in the gas phase (as discussed on p. 58). These difficulties are not limited to the donor-acceptor interaction but, in general, the complications mentioned above are neglected. It will therefore be assumed tentatively that the heats of reaction can give some idea of the strength of the donor-acceptor interaction, and the results will be compared with the simple theoretical discussion.

This assumption opens up a wide field of research, since a large number of at least qualitative results are available for comparisons of this type. The order of relative donor strengths reported for different phosphoryl compounds with $SnCl_4$ as acceptor molecule (p. 61) is a good example.

For a series of intimately related donor molecules differing only in outer substitution, the donor strength will be determined directly by the electron densities about the oxygen atom. In more general comparisons it must be remembered that the difference in electron mobility might also influence the order of donor strengths where these are very similar for a number of donors. Thus the availability of electron density is not necessarily a simple function of the magnitude of this density. However, in the case of outer substitution where no appreciable delocalization seems to be involved, this is a reasonable assumption to make.

The donor strengths for a series of phosphoryl compounds will then be a direct measure of the electronegativities of the different substituents. The following order is found: $CH_3 < C_6H_5 < C_4H_9O < C_6H_5O < Cl$. The phenyl thus behaves as a more electronegative group than methyl, with no suggestion of delocalization over the oxo-bond system. Similar orders are found for compounds containing S=O, $S\lessgtr^{O}_{O}$ and Se=O bonds. Compare also heats of formation for the free donors (1961: 54).

In corresponding compounds containing a C=O bond the expected electronegativity effect is found in the case of chlorine substitution; thus acyl halides are very poor donors and almost no donor properties remain in phosgene. It has also been found that in ketones the phenyl group behaves as though it were more electronegative than the methyl group.

The order predicted on the basis of the electronegativity effect is not observed in compounds such as esters and amides, for which appreciable delocalization of the bond has been assumed (see p. 91). Thus the amides are appreciably better donors than the ketones, and the difference between acetone and methyl acetate is much smaller than that expected from electronegativity differences; in these compounds delocalization almost balances the electronegativity effect. This balance is seen even more clearly in dimethyl carbonate which corresponds to a further substitution of $CH_3O$ for $CH_3$. Here the electronegativity effect is the same as that in the first step of substitution, while the delocalization effect is much smaller since delocalization already exists. This result can easily be predicted from elementary molecular orbital calculations. Accordingly, the reduction in donor strength should be more drastic on passing from $CH_3COOCH_3$ to $(CH_3O)_2CO$ than from $(CH_3)_2CO$ to $CH_3COOCH_3$. The actual differences in heats of reaction are 1.22 and 0.64 kcal/mole, respectively, in good agreement with prediction. The same trend is found in the ethyl compounds.

Similarly, the increase in donor strength due to the delocalization effect on passing from acetone to dimethylformamide is larger than for the next step in substitution, namely that from dimethylformamide to tetramethylurea.

It has also been found that the order of donor strengths for different acetates follows the accepted estimates of the relative electronegativities of the alkyl groups. Methyl acetate is thus a weaker donor than ethyl acetate, which is in turn weaker than iso-propyl acetate.

Final confirmation of these views regarding changes of heteropolarity and their importance to donor-acceptor reactions comes from a comparison of sulfoxides and sulfones as donor molecules. The addition of another oxygen atom to a sulfoxide leads, in the sulfone, to an electron withdrawal from the oxygen atom of the original S=O bond, and thus to a decreased electron density about that oxygen atom. In fact, the thermochemical studies made on these two types of compound show that the heats of reaction are of a different order of magnitude.

It is evident that thermochemical studies of donor-acceptor reactions using the same acceptor molecule offer an elegant method for studying the relative electron densities in a number of organic molecules with similar functions. In this connection, however, it should be borne in mind that electron mobility might also influence the results to some extent although the observed agreement with bond lengths shows that the factor cannot be very important in the compounds under consideration. The subsequent discussion will indicate some of the dangers of drawing sweeping conclusions based on the results of special cases. This is still more true of studies of kinetic mechanisms from which such conclusions are often drawn.

**Effect of substitution at the oxygen atom.** The approach to this problem is the same as that developed in the preceding section, beginning with an examination of the extent to which simple electronegativity effects can explain the experimental facts. As regards the oxo-compounds included in this book the atoms bonded to oxygen exhibit an increasing order of electronegativity as follows: $As < P < Se < S \sim C < N$, taking values from the accepted scale of electronegativities.

Comparing donors with the same outer substitution, the order of donor strength would be the reverse of that given above. So long as the consideration is limited to compounds with similar structure this is the order actually found, as reflected in the partial orders of donor strength derived from thermochemical studies: $(C_6H_5)_3AsO > (C_6H_5)_3PO$, $(C_6H_5)_2SeO >$ $> (C_6H_5)_2SO$, $(CH_3O)_2SeO > (CH_3O)_2SO$ and $SeOCl_2 > SOCl_2$.

However, when the different series are compared with each other, it is found that the selenium and sulfur compounds have appreciably higher donor strengths than would have been expected from the electronegativity scale. The donor strengths of the selenium compounds are the same as those of arsenic compounds, and those of the sulfur compounds are almost the same as those of phosphorus compounds .

Various possible explanations for this deviation from the simple electronegativity order will now be considered in the light of the experimental results.

The first of such possible explanations is that the accepted electronegativity scale cannot be applied directly to oxo-bonds, except for those with carbon. This would be so if empty *d*-orbitals on As, P or Se were used for $\pi$-bond formation; since the electronegativity scale does not relate to compounds containing such bonds. Accordingly, the net electronegativity for sulfur and selenium in oxo-compounds might be smaller than the accepted value, and the electron density about the oxygen atoms therefore higher than expected. (Cf. p. 102.)This should be reflected in the donor-acceptor bond lengths. The compounds $SnCl_4 \cdot 2POCl_3$ and $SnCl_4 \cdot 2SeOCl_2$ provide the only direct comparison and here the Sn—O bond length is seen to be shorter in the latter compound, 2.12 Å compared with 2.28 Å. The bond lengths in $SnCl_4 \cdot 2(CH_3)_2SO$ are also rather short, the average value being 2.14 Å. Much more evidence would be needed, however, before any definite conclusions could be drawn on this point.

It is clear that this cannot be the only explanation for the observed order of donor strength. For instance, the heat of reaction for the formation of the adduct $SbCl_5 \cdot POCl_3$ is much smaller than that for $SbCl_5 \cdot$ $\cdot (C_6H_5)_2SO$. However, the Sb—O bond lengths are very similar and the operation of some other factor is suspected. The structure determinations of adducts with sulfur and selenium compounds as donors have revealed one such possible factor. The discussion is here confined to tetravalent sulfur and selenium compounds which contain a lone electron pair and which have asymmetrical structures; hence the sulfur and selenium atoms are not enclosed by other atoms as are phosphorus and arsenic in their corresponding oxo-compounds. In the structures of adducts with $SeOCl_2$ or sulfoxides, some of the chlorine atoms in neighbouring molecules or in the acceptor part of the adduct approach more closely to the sulfur and selenium atoms than would be expected on the basis of van der Waals contacts. The distorted octahedral coordination around selenium in $SnCl_4 \cdot 2SeOCl_2$ which results is shown in Fig. 18 on p. 77. This extra interaction will influence the order of donor strengths as measured by calorimetric methods, and this complication demonstrates the importance of exact structure determinations in any discussion of chemical interaction.

The nature of this secondary interaction is not quite clear, but it is probably of an electrostatic nature and might originate in the partial dipoles being oriented so that interaction occurs.

Thus, it can be concluded that a rough comparison of oxo-compounds with different atoms bonded to the oxygen atom is possible on the basis of the accepted electronegativity scale, but that a more refined comparison requires more detailed discussion.

**Comparisons of oxo-compounds with ethers as donor molecules.** It has already been stated that in the $C=O$ bond the polarity of the $\pi$-bond is at least of the same order of magnitude as that of the $\sigma$-bond. Accordingly, in comparable ketones and ethers there should be a similar electron density about the oxygen atom thus giving rise to similar donor properties. This conclusion is confirmed by some qualitative studies using $SbCl_5$ and $SnCl_4$ as acceptor molecules (p. 61, 62) but the studies with $AlX_3$ acceptors (p. 60) indicate a clear difference between the two types of donor. Although these studies are not altogether appropriate for the present discussion, the observed differences are so large that it seems improbable that they can be due to different cohesion energies in the liquid state (reactions with D(l) have been studied). Thus it is found that $C_6H_5CHO$ is a much better donor than $(C_6H_5)_2O$ or $CH_3OC_6H_5$. Further thermochemical studies are necessary before the difference can be considered as definitely established, but even so the evidence is sufficiently strong to warrant a brief discussion of the possible causes.

It has already been mentioned that the purely electrostatic dipole-dipole interaction between the acceptor and donor molecules in the adduct might, under special conditions, be of great relative importance (p. 88). This could happen if the donor-acceptor interaction were very weak or if bonds in the acceptor molecule were strongly polar. The latter condition is fulfilled in $AlX_3$ acceptors, in contrast to $SbCl_5$ and $SnCl_4$. Ketones always have higher dipole moments than the corresponding ethers (e. g. 2.84 D for $(CH_3)_2CO$ and 1.29 D for $(CH_3)_2O$) and the dipole-dipole interaction should therefore be of greater significance for ketones. A still greater difference between ketones and ethers should then be expected upon adduct formation with $MgX_2$ acceptors. In fact the displacement studies place the ethers appreciably lower than the ketones in this case also (p. 59). The answers to this problem are far from satisfactory and indicate the need for more experimental work, planned in such a way that unambiguous conclusions can be reached.

In this connection some comment should be made about compounds analogous to the ethers in instances where other types of donor are used. These compounds contain bonds such as P—O—P and S—O—S, and a suitable example is that of $P_2O_3Cl_4$, which contains both P = O and P—O—P bonds:

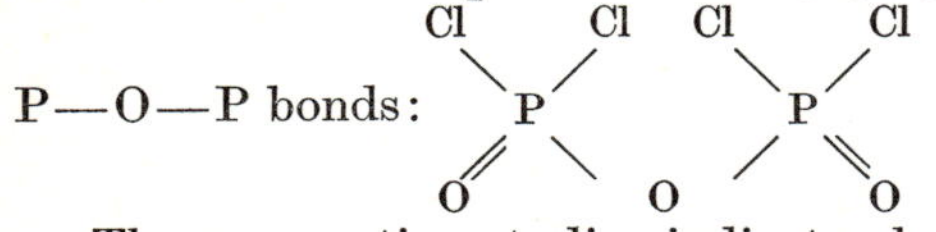


The preparative studies indicate clearly that only the non-bridging oxygen atoms are used as donor atoms (p. 36, 37). In the P = O bond the oxygen atom forms one $\sigma$- and one $\pi$-bond with phosphorus. The bridging oxygen atom on the other hand forms two different $\sigma$-bonds. (The argument is unaltered by the assumption that there are two $\pi$-bonds in the first case and a partial $\pi$-bond in the second case, but this alternative has not been considered since it is not warranted by any of the results under discussion; see, however, 1961 : 52.) As shown above (p. 93) it can be assumed that the polarity of the $\pi$-bonds is appreciably greater than that of the $\sigma$-bonds. The total electron density about the non-bridging oxygen atoms should therefore be higher than that about the bridging oxygen atoms, and the ability to form strong donor-acceptor bonds accordingly greater. The same arguments can be applied to phosphate esters in order to explain why the non-bridging oxygen atoms function as donors instead of those in the P—O—C bridge. Similar considerations apply to S = O and Se = O bonds, and it can be fairly claimed that the explanation is quite consistent with all the points discussed earlier. Note that while the same result is found for esters of carboxylic acids, in this instance it is due mainly to delocalization.

The latter case also constitutes an exception as regards the accepted electronegativity order as it applies to the substitution of $CH_3O$ for $CH_3$, while this effect is not observed in oxo-compounds containing oxo-bonds other than C = O.

**Comparisons of oxo-compounds with amines as donor molecules.** The comparison with amines introduces a new factor into the discussions, that is a donor-acceptor bond containing a *different donor atom*, namely nitrogen. This rather obvious fact is often overlooked in discussions of this type and quite recently FYFE found it necessary to emphasize this fundamental distinction (1958: 46). It is not only the ionization energy which is of importance but also the energy which is released when an electron pair bond is formed. Provided that both the donor and the acceptor atoms remain the same, comparisons of different donor-acceptor bonds can lead to surprisingly accurate predictions of the variations in bond strength (see above). However, some additional knowledge is needed to permit predictions when either the donor or the acceptor atom is varied. It seems reasonable to suppose that when oxygen and nitrogen atoms are compared as donors, their relative sizes are of limited importance. Thus, if an electron pair donor-acceptor bond is formed, the difference in bond strength should be determined mainly by the ionization energies, which are measures of the availability of the lone electron pair for bond formation. As amines have lower ionization energies than oxo-compounds, it is to be expected that they will form stronger donor-acceptor bonds (1958: 47). This is undoubtedly true in the case of compounds with acceptor molecules such as $BF_3$, $AlCl_3$, $SnCl_4$ and $SbCl_5$, although precise information is often lacking. It would be of particular interest to study $MgX_2$ adducts, in which the acceptor molecule favours a dipole-dipole interaction, in order to find out whether in this case oxo-compounds are better donors than amines.

There is an interesting point concerning a structural difference between 1:2 adducts with oxo-compounds as donors and those with amines. All the available evidence seems to suggest that amines give *trans* adducts while oxo-compounds give *cis* adducts. If more complete experimental information confirms this, it will be necessary to find a theoretical explanation to account for the effect.

**Effect of substitution at the acceptor atom.** There is relatively little information concerning the effect of substitution at the acceptor atom on donor-acceptor bonds with oxo-compounds. Structural evidence on this point is lacking, but affinity studies indicate that in many cases the effect of substitution is precisely what might be expected from a consideration of the electronegativities of the substituents. This is exemplified by the order found for $ZrX_4$ adducts with $POCl_3$ in $C_6H_5NO_2$ (p. 59), and for alkoxy-substituted $ZrX_4$ adducts with methylacetate (p. 60). Of greater interest are the deviations from the expected order; for instance, $BCl_3$ is a better acceptor than $BF_3$ using $C_6H_5NO_2$ as the donor (p. 60) and $AlBr_3$ is better than $AlCl_3$ using $(C_6H_5)_2CO$ as the donor molecule (p. 60). An interpretation of this reversal of order has already been given (p. 98), namely that the rehybridization energy is larger for $BF_3$ than for $BCl_3$ owing to the greater strength of the delocalized $\pi$-bond in $BF_3$. The situation would be more satisfactory if experimental evidence could be obtained to show that the B—O bond is really stronger in the $BF_3$ adduct in accordance with the electronegativity prediction. More systematic studies should be made on the effect of step-wise substitution at the acceptor atom.

Comment should be made at this point on the difference between $SbCl_5$ and $SbCl_3$ as acceptor molecules. The former is a much better acceptor than the latter, and there are several possible reasons for this. The greater number of polar bonds in $SbCl_5$ can be expected to reduce the electron density about the antimony atom, so that it becomes a better acceptor. In addition, the increase in stability attending rehybridization from a trigonal bipyramidal to an octahedral coordination (p. 98) may also be significant. The structure of $SbCl_3$ corresponds to $sp^3$ hybridization (1956: 35), and changes to the seemingly less stable $sp^3d$ hybridization in 1:1 adducts and to $sp^3d^2$ hybridization in 1:2 adducts. More knowledge about Sb—O bond lengths in $SbCl_3$ adducts is needed before this discussion can be amplified.

**Comparisons between different acceptor atoms.** This discussion is based on one of the few orders for acceptor strengths which have been firmly established, namely that $AlCl_3$ is a better acceptor than $BCl_3$ using $C_6H_5NO_2$ as the donor molecule (given by 1950: 6 and 1956: 17 after due consideration of the cohesion energies). This order seems to apply in the general case, since it has also been found with other donors (1958: 47). Note also that $GaCl_3$ is a better acceptor than $BCl_3$ (but weaker than $AlCl_3$) using $CH_3COCl$ and amines as donors (1958: 47).

Although it has already been emphasized that predictions based on relative electronegativities can only be made when either the donor or the acceptor atom is the same, it is instructive to examine the results of such a prediction in the above case. As boron is more electro-negative than aluminium, $BCl_3$ should be a stronger acceptor than $AlCl_3$, i. e. the reverse of what has been found. The difference in atomic size can have two opposite effects. In general a larger atomic size should result in a weaker interaction, so that again $BCl_3$ should be a stronger acceptor than $AlCl_3$. On the other hand, the small size of the boron atom might lead to steric interference, which would reduce the heats of reaction and increase the donor-acceptor bond length. It has been claimed that this is the main cause of the reversed order of acceptor strengths (1958: 47) and there is a large body of work by H. C. Brown and his collaborators which proves that when boron is the acceptor atom, steric interference is of some significance.

Another attractive explanation is that the loss of $\pi$-bond energy could be much larger for $BCl_3$ than for $AlCl_3$, but this does not agree with the calculations made by Cotton and Leto (1959: 59).

It is interesting to compare these results with the attempts made by Strohmeier to compare the relative acceptor strengths of dialkylmetal compounds using dioxane as the donor molecule, on the basis of comparative dielectric constant studies (1956: 36, 37). He finds the order Mg $>$ Be, i. e. a reversal similar to that discussed above.

More studies are needed before it can be safely claimed that the interpretation given here for the reversal of order, has been definitely established.

**Comparison with thio-substituted oxo-compounds.** There are a number of factors to be considered when the donor strengths of ketones are compared with those of thioketones etc. The larger size of the sulfur atom should lead to weaker interaction; the lower ionization energy should lead to stronger interaction. It is impossible to make any predictions about the balance between these two factors, which have to be considered for all types of acceptor atoms. With transition elements as acceptor atoms there is a further possibility of $\pi$-bond formation between filled $d$-orbitals from the acceptor atom and unfilled $d$-orbitals on the donor atom.

There is little experimental evidence with regard to this point, but it is obvious that comparisons should lead to very different results for different oxo-compounds. With $SbCl_5$ and $SnCl_4$ as acceptors the donor strengths of amides and thioamides are rather similar, while $PSCl_3$ is a much weaker donor than $POCl_3$. This should be compared with the fact that with the same acceptors, thioethers are stronger than ethers.

Since with these acceptors, the size factor is the same and $\pi$-bond formation of the type mentioned above is impossible, the determining factor should be the different availabilities of the lone pair electrons, that is, in the ionization energies.

In any case it is clearly an over-simplification to attempt a division of acceptor atoms into two groups according to their preferences for oxygen or sulfur as donor atoms (1958: 48). The relative order between donor molecules containing oxygen and sulfur atoms depends upon a balance between differences in atomic size, availability of lone pairs of electrons and possible $\pi$-bond formation.

**The coordination around the acceptor atom.** It is unnecessary to repeat here all the instances in which it is difficult to understand or predict which of two possible coordinations is obtained. The experimental evidence suggests that strong donor-acceptor interaction (corresponding to appreciable electron density transfer) favours tetrahedral coordination in zinc adducts (in contrast to the octahedral coordination in some other compounds) and also in mercury adducts (in contrast to the linear coordination preserved only in cases of weak interaction). However, no satisfactory explanations have been given to account for this situation.

### h) Formation of ions from adduct molecules

It has been shown in the experimental section that the increased ionic conductivity in solutions of adduct molecules in different solvents has attracted much interest, and that much experimental work has been done on this problem. In this chapter there will be an attempt to show why ions are formed from adduct molecules. Since the adducts are neutral, ion formation will always be connected with some type of exchange between a molecule and a halide ion. This can be described formally either as internal exchange or as halide ion transfer, and both alternatives will be considered.

**Internal exchange between ions and molecules.** The internal exchange reaction in, for example, the adduct $SbCl_5 \cdot D$ will be $2SbCl_5D = SbCl_4D_2^+ + SbCl_6^-$. The extent of such self-dissociation is favoured by a high dielectric constant in the solvent if this has no donor properties. However, it is also necessary to determine to what extent the nature of D can influence self-dissociation.

Considering the $SbCl_4^+$ ion, one $Cl^-$ and one donor molecule can be added in two different ways:

(1) a) $SbCl_4^+ + Cl^- = SbCl_5$ b) $SbCl_5 + D = SbCl_5D$

or (2) a) $SbCl_4^+ + Cl^- = SbCl_5$ b) $SbCl_5 + Cl^- = SbCl_6^-$

a′) $SbCl_4^+ + D = SbCl_4D^+$ b′) $SbCl_4D^+ + D = SbCl_4D_2^+$

Reactions (1a), (2a) and (2b) are independent of the nature of D while reactions (1b), (2a′) and (2b′) are favoured by a high donor strength in D. The two latter reactions lead to self-dissociation and involve positively charged species as acceptors, so that an increase in the donor strength of D should increase the heats of reaction for (2a′) and (2b′) more than for (1b). (Entropy changes should be independent of D.)

This means that self-dissociation should be favoured by a high donor strength in D. If the self-dissociation takes place in an excess of donor D as solvent, the order of self-dissociation might be changed as a result of the different dielectric constants of the donors. These predictions have not been confirmed by any systematic experimental work. However, they are necessary for any further consideration of the subject, and as the assumptions from which they are derived are well founded it seems reasonable to continue the discussion on this basis.

**Halide ion transfer.** If the donor molecule contains halogen atoms, halide ion transfer reactions are also possible. Consider a donor $D^+Cl^-$ and the two reactions (1) $SbCl_5 + D^+Cl^- = SbCl_5 \cdot D^+Cl^-$ and (2a) $D^+Cl^- = D^+ + Cl^-$, (2b) $SbCl_5 + Cl^- = SbCl_6^-$ corresponding to the net reaction (2) $SbCl_5 + D^+Cl^- = D^+ + SbCl_6^-$. It is difficult to discuss the relative heats of reaction for (1) and (2) in general terms, since both a donor-acceptor bond formation and a dissociation reaction (with attendant solvation of the ions thus formed) are involved in the calculations. (The entropy changes are again independent of the nature of $D^+Cl^-$.)

A specific example is provided by a comparison of $POCl_3$ and $C_6H_5POCl_2$. The latter is the stronger donor (p. 102) and should thus give a stronger donor-acceptor interaction in reaction (1). On the other hand this compound should contain the weaker P—Cl bond owing to the "electronegativity effect" discussed earlier (p. 94). It should thus be easier to dissociate the P—Cl bond. Once again the effects counterbalance each other and it is impossible to predict the net effect and to decide which compound provides the more favourable conditions for P—Cl bond dissociation. If the reaction is carried out in an excess of the donor, the dielectric constant of the donor must also be taken into account. $SbCl_5$ is a better chloride ion acceptor in $POCl_3$ than in $C_6H_5POCl_2$ (1961: 37, 41, 42), and since the dielectric constant of $POCl_3$ is lower than that of $C_6H_5POCl_2$, the donor-acceptor interaction energy should be the most important factor in the above-mentioned balance of energies. The conclusions reached concerning the chloride ion acceptor strength of $SbCl_5$ were based on competitive reactions in the donors used as solvents, but the results are directly applicable to this discussion. The opposing effects on competitive chloride ion transfer of donor strength and dielectric constant variations have been dealt with in the papers quoted above, but without consideration being given to their relevance to internal halide ion transfer.

Here the argument has been extended in order to see how the two self-dissociation reactions are influenced by the strengths of the donors and it has been found that internal exchange is favoured by increasing donor strength. However, in comparing these two possible methods of dissociation it is also necessary to take into account the different entropy changes of the two reactions. In inert solvents the internal exchange reaction should be independent of concentration, while halide ion transfer should increase with increasing dilution.

**Competitive halide ion transfer reactions.** The titration reactions mentioned in the experimental section (p. 55) should be influenced by competitive adduct formation in solvents with donor properties. Thus, provided that the donor strength of the solvent is great enough, no transfer reactions should be observed. This has been found to be the case with $(C_4H_9O)_3PO$ as solvent in contrast to $POCl_3$ and $C_6H_5POCl_2$. However, if halide ion transfer reactions are obtained with alkylammonium halides then this proves that complex formation is stronger with the halide ion than with the solvent donor molecule. This difference should increase with the strength of the acceptor since the interaction energies can be assumed to be roughly proportional to the acceptor strengths. It follows that $SbCl_5$ is a stronger halide ion acceptor than $TiCl_4$, and a weaker chloride ion donor. The whole sequence of halide ion acceptor and donor strengths determined by GUTMANN and his collaborators can be discussed in the same way. Halide ion transfer of this kind is also found in the ternary compound $[TiCl_3(POCl_3)]SbCl_6$ (p. 48).

With even stronger donors, a reversal of the relative halide ion acceptor and donor strengths for $SbCl_5$ and $TiCl_4$ should finally be obtained, but no instance of this has been studied as yet.

The above discussion is rather brief, since the problem is not a major one in adduct chemistry. The treatment is also incomplete, and does not pretend to answer all the questions regarding different possible dissociation and halide ion transfer reactions. The main intention has been to show where further experimental work can help to distinguish between the different possible reactions which produce ions of adduct molecules in solution. The experimental methods of studying this problem have already been discussed (p. 57).

## i) Decomposition reactions

In decomposition reactions the path of the reaction is often determined by the activation energy. It is beyond the scope of this book to give a theoretical discussion of the factors which influence these activation energies. However, some attempt will be made to find out how far simple energy considerations (thermodynamics) can be used to interpret the decomposition reactions mentioned in the systematic section. This discussion is rather similar to the treatment of dissociation reactions in the preceding chapter.

The simplest case of elimination, with the formation of HCl, corresponds to competition for the best donor between the acceptor halide and the proton. In the case of moderately weak acids, this donor will always be the acid anion, since HCl is a strong acid and $Cl^-$ accordingly a very weak donor. There is therefore no energetic reason why the elimination reaction should take place if the proton is a stronger acceptor than the acceptor halide. This situation is the same as that occurring in the hydrolysis of various chlorides. Thus NaCl is not hydrolyzed at all, $MgCl_2$ and $AlCl_3$ are only partially hydrolysed, while $SiCl_4$ and $PCl_5$ show a progressive increase in hydrolysis with the formation of silicic and phosphoric acids of different types. In this case the proton can successfully compete with a highly charged ion such as $Al^{3+}$, although not with $Si^{4+}$.

This is a rather simplified explanation, but it undoubtedly supplies the main reason for such hydrolyses.

Returning to the question of elimination reactions with acceptor halides, it is clear that the tendency to undergo this type of reaction should follow the tendency to hydrolysis very closely. Thus $SbCl_5$ fumes in air, and it also competes successfully with $H^+$ for the anion of a carboxylic acid, leading to reactions such as $SbCl_5 + CH_3COOH = SbCl_4(CH_3COO) + HCl$. At higher temperatures reactions of this type will be favoured by the elimination of HCl as a gas.

However, there is no doubt that adduct formation will also take place, so that in general the resulting formulae will be in accordance with an octahedral configuration around the antimony atom in the specific case. In $SbCl_5 \cdot CH_3COOH$ the direct effect of adduct formation is also an increase in the acidity of the acetic acid (see p. 47) which will favour decomposition.

The kinetic aspect of the problem will be considered briefly. It appears that the kinetics of the hydrolysis of an $SbCl_5$ molecule are influenced by adduct formation. The free $SbCl_5$ molecule first adds an $H_2O$ molecule, and then elimination takes place. If another donor molecule which is a stronger donor than water is present the rate of hydrolysis is appreciably reduced. For example, $SbCl_5 \cdot POCl_3$ is rapidly hydrolyzed in air while $SbCl_5 \cdot (CH_3)_3PO$ can be kept in moist air for long periods without decomposition. In the first case it is probable that $H_2O$ (comparable with an ether in donor strength) first displaces the $POCl_3$ molecule, after which HCl elimination begins; in the second case this kind of attack is not possible since the phosphine oxide is a better donor than water. An explanation of this difference purely in terms of energetics is impossible.

The elimination of alkyl halides can be discussed in a manner similar to that used for the elimination of HCl, but the reaction mechanisms are generally very complicated and cannot be treated here.

Using esters as donors two different decomposition reactions are possible, corresponding to the alternative formation of alkyl halides RCl or acyl chlorides RCOCl (p. 81).

These two reactions correspond to a splitting of the ester RCOOR′ into either $RCOO^-$ and $R'^+$ or $RCO^+$ and $OR'^-$. If energetic considerations are significant then the effect of adduct formation should be demonstrated by the choice of one or other of these reaction paths depending on the nature of the acceptor. The direct effect of adduct formation is a withdrawal of electron density from the oxygen atom of the $C=O$ bond; this leads to a weakening of the $C=O$ bond, a *strengthening* of the C—O bond (p. 95) and a less pronounced weakening of the O—R′ bond. Strong donor-acceptor interaction should therefore favour the elimination of R′Cl rather than the formation of RCOCl. In fact R′Cl is formed using $SnCl_4$ and $ZrCl_4$ as acceptors, and RCOCl using $BCl_3$ and $SiCl_4$. No comparative studies have been made between the strengths of these acceptors so that the question remains unanswered for lack of experimental results. This brief consideration does show, however, that more experimental work is needed and gives some indication of the direction it might take to provide the most useful results.

As a rule, exchange reactions between halogen and oxygen will occur if the difference in acceptor strength is large enough, and the oxygen atoms transfer to the strongest acceptor. The example of exchange between $SiCl_4$ and $(C_6H_5)_2SO$ shown on p. 81 can be compared with the exchange between $POCl_3$ and $SeOCl_2$ which leads to the formation of $P_2O_5$ and $SeCl_4$ (p. 38). The same complication occurs in the reaction between $BCl_3$ and $SeOCl_2$ (p. 45).

## j) The catalytic effect of adduct formation

In view of the confusion which exists in this field it would be pretentious to attempt a deep account of the fundamentals underlying the many catalytic effects reported in the experimental section. On the other hand, the reasonably consistent picture of the chemistry of these adducts with oxo-compounds which has been built up, encourages the belief that it should be possible to apply these concepts in some way to a consideration of catalytic effects. Lack of knowledge concerning the reaction mechanism and the step at which the adduct molecule is involved constitutes the source of the problem. With a little exaggeration it might be claimed that it is possible to explain *all types* of reactions and therefore *no* reactions. This apparent contradiction will be demonstrated by an example.

Consider the effect of adduct formation on acyl halides and esters. Since they both give adducts with acceptor molecules, adduct formation in the two instances will influence the thermodynamics of all reactions in which they take part. This need not be significant to the path if another stage in the reaction constitutes the rate-determining step. Predictions regarding the effect of adduct formation can be made as follows. With the acyl halide as the oxo-compound a weakening of the C=O bond and a strengthening of the C—Cl will occur, whereas with the ester a weakening the C=O bond and a strengthening of the C—O bond will result. These effects might or might not have a strong influence on the mechanism of the reactions studied. It is also possible that it is not bond weakening or bond strengthening that is of significance but rather the altered electron density distribution. In the present example the most obvious effect is the increased net positive charge on the carbon atom in the C=O bond (see p. 80). The relative importance of these two effects, namely changes in bond strength and electron density, cannot be predicted and the choice of explanation often depends upon whichever is most convenient for interpreting the experimental results. Thus in Friedel-Craft acylation, the electron density change is involved (p. 84). The fact is, however, that much more systematic work is needed before valid rationalizations can be made in this field.

### k) Summary

In giving a brief summary of these theoretical considerations, it seems fair to say that a theoretical basis exists which is very simple and not overloaded with special assumptions. The next step in the theoretical treatment of donor-acceptor interaction with oxo-compounds will require a much more systematic investigation and more accurate experimental work. The need for well-planned thermochemical and structural studies should be particularly stressed, since progress from a qualitative to a quantitative theory must depend on the determination of heats of reactions, which show the total interaction, and of bond lengths and bond angles which illustrate the details of the interaction.

## 27. References

Some of the references in the following section refer to Zentralblatt or Chemical Abstracts. Such references have been preferred when the original was not available to the author, or when it seemed possible that the original might not be generally available. References to Russian work usually quote the original, even in cases where the journals are available in translation. The Russian names have been given in English, generally according to the conventions adopted in Chemical Abstracts. The author cannot claim, however, that any of these rules have been followed strictly.

After each reference the pages on which it has been mentioned in the text are indicated. The system adopted replaces an author list which, in general, is of little interest other than providing satisfaction for a rather unscientific curiosity. For the sake of simplification all names are given without initials in the reference list. The minor confusion which this might occasion if two different authors share the same surname is easily eliminated by the reader who is sufficiently interested to look at the original paper.

In conclusion, it should be mentioned that all the private communications quoted for 1962 will be published, most of them at about the same time as this book. The information they give has been considered essential to the discussions and in some instances even preliminary results have been included. Where this has been done an indication has been included in the reference list.

page

**1857**

1. Neubauer and Kerner: Liebigs Ann. Chem. **101**, 337 — 19, 20, 31

**1861**

1. Hofmann: Liebigs Ann. Chem. Suppl. **1**, 1 — 35

**1862**

1. Pebal: Liebigs Ann. Chem. **120**, 194 — 39

**1865**

1. WEBER: Ann. Physik (2) **125**, 328 — 45, 46

**1867**

1. WEBER: Ann. Physik (2) **132**, 452 — 37

**1871**

1. GUSTAVSON: Z. Chem. (N. F.) **7, 417** — 36

**1873**

1. DEMARÇAY: Bull. Soc. chim. Fr. (2) **20**, 127 — 26

**1877**

1. WEHRLIN and GIRAUD: C. R. Acad. Sci. (Paris) **85**, 288 — 37

**1879**

1. LANDOLPH: Ber. dtsch. chem. Ges. **12**, 1578 — 21
2. PIUTTI: Gazz. chim. ital. **9**, 538 — 38

**1880**

1. GUSTAVSON: Ber. dtsch. chem. Ges. **13**, 157 — 23
2. BERTRAND: Bull. Soc. chim. Fr. (2) **33**, 403 — 32
3. FLEISSNER: Ber. dtsch. chem. Ges. **13**, 1665 — 35, 39
4. BERTRAND: Bull. Soc. chim. Fr. (2) **34**, 631 — 32

**1886**

1. ANDRÉ: C. R. Acad. Sci. (Paris) **102**, 115 — 20, 21, 30, 31

**1892**

1. VOLHARD: Liebigs Ann. Chem. **267**, 172 — 20

**1893**

1. PERRIER: Bull. Soc. chim. Fr. (3) **9**, 1049 — 22, 23, 32, 83
2. STOCKHAUSEN and GATTERMANN: Ber. dtsch. chem. Ges. **25**, 3521 — 34

**1894**

1. GASSELIN: Ann. chim. phys. (7) **3**, 57 — 21
2. PERRIER: Bull. Soc. chim. Fr. (3) **11**, 926 — 23

**1896**

1. RUSPAGGIARI: Gazz. chim. ital. **27**, I 1 — 21
2. PERRIER: Gmelin **35**: Al, part B, 216 — 23
3. PERRIER: Bull. Soc. chim. Fr. (3) **15**, 322 — 22

**1898**

1. SCHIFF: Liebigs Ann. Chem. **299**, 235 — 31
2. KLAGES and ALLENDORFF: Ber. dtsch. chem. Ges. **31**, 1298 — 47

**1899**

1. PARTHEIL: Arch. Pharm. (Weinheim) **237**, 121 — 39

**1900**

1. BOESEKEN: Rec. Trav. chim. Pays-Bas **19**, 19 — 22, 23, 32, 43
2. PRANDTL and HOFMANN: Ber. dtsch. chem. Ges. **33**, 2981 — 31
3. KOHLER: Amer. chem. J. **24**, 385 — 43, 50

**1901**

1. BOESEKEN: Rec. Trav. chim. Pays-Bas **20**, 102 — 22, 32, 81, 84
2. ROSENHEIM and STELLMANN: Ber. dtsch. chem. Ges. **34**, 3377 — 28, 29, 32, 35

**1902**

1. Klages: Ber. dtsch. chem Ges. **35**, 2633 — 18
2. Stollé: Ber. dtsch. chem. Ges. **35**, 1590 — 20
3. Kohler: Amer. chem. J. **27**, 241 — 22, 23, 32
4. Rosenheim and Loewenstamm: Ber. dtsch. chem. Ges. **35**, 1115 — 28, 32, 81

**1903**

1. Gernez: C. R. Acad. Sci. (Paris) **137**, 255 — 20
2. Rosenheim, Loewenstamm and Singer: Ber. dtsch. chem. Ges. **36**, 1833 — 25, 26, 28, 81
3. Rosenheim, Samter and Davidsohn: Z. anorg. Chem. **35**, 424 — 27
4. Boeseken: Rec. Trav. chim. Pays-Bas **22**, 315 — 30, 33
5. Oddo and Tealdi: Gazz. chim. ital. **33**, II 427 — 35, 36, 37
6. Ruff and Ipsen: Ber. dtsch. chem. Ges. **36**, 1777 — 37
7. Rosenheim and Loewenstamm: Z. anorg. Chem. **37**, 394 — 39
8. Dilthey: Ber. dtsch. chem. Ges. **36**, 923, 1595 — 81

**1904**

1. Sudborough, Hibbert and Beard: Proc. chem. Soc. **20**, 165 — 17, 18
2. Schenck: Hoppe-Seylers Z. physiol. Chem. **43**, 72 — 20, 23
3. Erdmann: Ber. dtsch. chem. Ges. **37**, 4571 — 20
4. Willstätter and Pummerer: Ber. dtsch. chem. Ges. **37**, 3740 — 20
5. Walker and Spencer: J. chem. Soc. **85**, 1106 — 23, 34
6. Rosenheim and Levy: Ber. dtsch. chem. Ges. **37**, 3662 — 24, 25, 27, 28, 30
7. Straus: Ber. dtsch. chem. Ges. **37**, 3277 — 30
8. Boeseken: Rec. Trav. chim. Pays-Bas **23**, 98 — 34
9. Ruff: Ber. dtsch. chem. Ges. **37**, 4513 — 39

**1905**

1. Ahrens and Stapler: Ber. dtsch. chem. Ges. **38**, 1296, 3259 — 18
2. Rosenheim and Levy: Z. anorg. Chem. **43**, 34 — 39

**1906**

1. Aten: Z. phys. Chem. **54**, 121 — 20
2. Mensutkin: C. **1906** II, 1719 — 32
3. Pickard and Kenyon: J. chem. Soc. **89**, 262 — 35, 39, 47

**1907**

1. Mensutkin: Z. anorg. Chem. **53**, 26 — 17, 23
2. Mensutkin: Z. anorg. Chem. **54**, 89 — 18
3. Meyer and Hantzsch: Ber. dtsch. chem. Ges. **40**, 3479 — 26
4. Rosenheim and Hertzmann: Ber. dtsch. chem. Ges. **40**, 810 — 27, 81
5. Hofmann and Ott: Ber. dtsch. chem. Ges. **40**, 4930 — 42

**1908**

1. Meyer: Ber. dtsch. chem. Ges. **41**, 2568 — 19, 20, 23, 24, 28, 30
2. Clayton: J. chem. Soc. **93**, 524 — 20
3. Lenher: J. Amer. chem. Soc. **30**, 737 — 38

**1909**

1. Mensutkin: Z. anorg. Chem. **61**, 100 — 18
2. Mensutkin: Z. anorg. Chem. **61**, 113 — 18
3. Naumann: Ber. dtsch. chem. Ges. **42**, 3789 — 18
4. Mascarelli: Gazz. chim. ital. **39**, I 251 — 34
5. Mensutkin: Z. anorg. Chem. **62**, 45 — 58

**1910**

1. Gomberg and Cone: Liebigs Ann. Chem. **376**, 183 — 18, 19, 20, 24
2. Meyer: Ber. dtsch. chem. Ges. **43**, 157 — 20, 22, 24, 29, 47
3. Mensutkin: C. **1910** II, 154 — 23

4. KABLUKOW and SSACHANOW: C. **1910** I, 912 — 23, 24
5. PFEIFFER: Liebigs Ann. Chem. **376**, 285 — 24, 25, 26, 32
6. RÖHLER: Z. Elektrochem. **16**, 419 — 31, 81
7. MENSUTKIN: C. **1910** I, 1240 — 34
8. MENSUTKIN: C. **1910** II, 381 — 35
9. EPHRAIM and GUREWITSCH: Ber. dtsch. chem. Ges. **43**, 138 — 43

**1911**

1. PFEIFFER: Liebigs Ann. Chem. **383**, 92 — 23, 24, 25, 26, 80
2. FOOTE and WALDEN: J. Amer. chem. Soc. **33**, 1032 — 31
3. MENSUTKIN: C. **1911** I, 481 — 32

**1912**

1. REDDELIEN: Liebigs Ann. Chem. **388**, 165 — 19, 85
2. PLOTNIKOV: C. **1912** I, 1839 — 22
3. MENSUTKIN: C. **1912** I, 806 — 28, 33
4. MENSUTKIN: C. **1912** II, 1436 — 35
5. BASSETT and TAYLOR: Z. anorg. Chem. **73**, 75 — 35
6. MENSUTKIN: C. **1912** II, 1437 — 43

**1913**

1. PFEIFFER: Liebigs Ann. Chem. **398**, 137 — 24
2. MENSUTKIN: C. **1913** I, 804 — 28
3. BOESEKEN: Rec. Trav. chim. Pays-Bas **32**, 1 — 32, 49
4. MENSUTKIN: C. **1913** I, 805 — 34
5. KURNAKOV and ZEMCUZNY: Z. phys. Chem. **83**, 481 — 51
6. CURRIE: J. Amer. chem. Soc. **35**, 1061 — 82

**1914**

1. PFEIFFER and HALPERIN: Z. anorg. Chem. **87**, 335 — 25
2. PFEIFFER: Z. anorg. Chem. **87**, 235 — 25
3. BOESEKEN and VAN OCKENBURG: Rec. Trav. chim. Pays-Bas **33**, 317 — 49

**1915**

1. SIMONIS and ELIAS: Ber. dtsch. chem. Ges. **48**, 1499 — 12, 20, 29, 30
2. PFEIFFER and WITTKA: Ber. dtsch. chem. Ges. **48**, 1289 — 13, 21
3. JACOBS: C. **1915** I, 1254 — 31

**1916**

1. PFEIFFER: Liebigs Ann. Chem. **412**, 253 — 24, 34
2. FRY and DONNELLY: J. Amer. chem. Soc. **38**, 1923 — 38
3. OLIVIER: Rec. Trav. chim. Pays-Bas **35**, 166 — 43

**1917**

1. GANGLOFF and HENDERSON: J. Amer. chem. Soc. **39**, 1420 — 22, 23

**1918**

1. OLIVIER: Rec. Trav. chim. Pays-Bas **37**, 205 — 32
2. OLIVIER: Rec. Trav. chim. Pays-Bas **37**, 92 — 43

**1919**

1. JANTSCH and URBACH: Helv. chim. Acta **2**, 490 — 27

**1921**

1. HESS and RHEINBOLDT: Ber. dtsch. chem. Ges. **54**, 2043 — 18

**1922**

1. HANTZSCH: Ber. dtsch. chem. Ges. **55**, 953 — 24
2. SILBERRAD: J. chem. Soc. **121**, 1015 — 44

**1923**

1. Weinland and Schmid: C. **1923** III, 62 — 13
2. Belladen and Astengo: C. **1923** III, 1266 — 20, 31
3. Vorländer and Eichwald: Ber. dtsch. chem. Ges. 56, 1150 — 20
4. Kurnakow, Perelmuter and Kanow: C. **1923** I, 1538 — 25, 52
5. Lindner and Feit: Z. anorg. Chem. **132**, 10 — 29
6. Wise: J. Amer. chem. Soc. **45**, 1233 — 45, 46

**1924**

1. Hess and Wustrow: Liebigs Ann. Chem. **437**, 256 — 17, 18
2. Coucoulesco: C. **1924** II, 22 — 18
3. Weygand: Ber. dtsch. chem. Ges. **57**, 413 — 24
4. Hieber: Liebigs Ann. Chem. **439**, 97 — 24, 25, 28, 50, 59
5. Kurnakow: Z. anorg. Chem. **135**, 81 — 25, 28, 52
6. van Arkel and de Boer: Z. anorg. Chem. **141**, 289 — 37
7. Tschelinzeff: Bull. Soc. chim. Fr. (4) **35**, 741 — 60

**1925**

1. Pfeiffer: Liebigs Ann. Chem. **441**, 228 — 16, 81
2. Hieber: Liebigs Ann. Chem. **444**, 249 — 25
3. Fricke and Havestadt: Z. anorg. Chem. **146**, 121 — 17, 34
4. Fricke and Ruschhaupt: Z. anorg. Chem. **146**, 103 — 17, 82
5. Meisenheimer: Liebigs Ann. Chem. **442**, 180 — 17, 18
6. Arndt and Pusch: Ber. dtsch. chem. Ges. **58**, 1648 — 24
7. Schönberg: Ber. dtsch. chem. Ges. **58**, 1793 — 24
8. Hieber and Wagner: Liebigs Ann. Chem. **444**, 256 — 25
9. Vanstone: J. chem. Soc. **127**, 550 — 29
10. Tschelinzeff: Bull. Soc. chim. Fr. (4) **37**, 176 — 60

**1926**

1. Dilthey and Berres: J. prakt. Chem. (2) **112**, 299 — 19
2. Brass and Mosl: Ber. dtsch. chem. Ges. **59**, 1266 — 25

**1927**

1. Tschelinzeff and Nasaroff: Bull. Soc. chim. Fr. (4) **41**, 805 — 17, 18
2. Meerwein: Liebigs Ann. Chem. **455**, 227 — 21, 48
3. Costenau: Ber. dtsch. chem. Ges. **60**, 2223 — 24
4. Scagliarini and Tartarini: C. **1927** I, 412 — 26
5. Jantsch: J. prakt. Chem. (2) **115**, 7 — 27, 81
6. Reihlen and Hake: Liebigs Ann. Chem. **452**, 47 — 34, 35
7. Stranathan and Strong: J. phys. Chem. **31**, 1420 — 52

**1928**

1. Fricke and Röbke: Z. anorg. Chem. **170**, 25 — 17
2. Pfeiffer, Kollbach and Haack: Liebigs Ann. Chem. **460**, 138 — 22, 23
3. Pfeiffer and Haack: Liebigs Ann. Chem. **460**, 156 — 22

**1929**

1. Asahina and Dono: Hoppe-Seylers Z. physiol. Chem. **186**, 133 — 20, 21, 29
2. Uschakow: Z. anorg. Chem. **183**, 140 — 22
3. Garner and Sugden: J. chem. Soc. 1298 — 36
4. Bond and Stephens: J. Amer. chem. Soc. **51**, 2910 — 44

**1930**

1. Răşçanu: C. **1930** II, 897 — 13
2. Bell, Powlands, Bamford, Thomas and Jones: J. chem. Soc. 1927 — 17, 18, 19, 30
3. Brus and Vebra: C. R. Acad. Sci. (Paris) **191**, 667 — 19, 28
4. Machemer: J. prakt. Chem. (2) **127**, 109 — 24
5. De Carli: Chem. Abstr. **24**, 3153 — 34

6. Davidson: J. phys. Chem. **34**, 1215 — 48
7. Riddell and Noller: J. Amer. chem. Soc. **52**, 4365 — 83

**1931**

1. Bowlus and Nieuwland: J. Amer. chem. Soc. **53**, 3835 — 21, 22, 48
2. Răşçanu: C. **1931** II, 1996 — 29
3. Ulich: Z. phys. Chem. Bodenstein-Festband 423 — 50

**1932**

1. Morgan and Taylor: J. chem. Soc. **134**, 1497 — 21
2. Meerwein and Maier-Hüser: J. prakt. Chem. (2) **134**, 51 — 22, 26, 32, 49
3. Sugden and Waloff: J. chem. Soc. **134**, 1492 — 22
4. Nespital: Z. phys. Chem. **B 16**, 153 — 22, 32, 34, 78
5. Hertel and Demmer: Liebigs Ann. Chem. **499**, 134 — 26, 35
6. Locket: J. chem. Soc. **134**, 1501 — 41
7. Ulich, Hertel and Nespital: Z. phys. Chem. **B 17**, 21 — 50, 78
8. Wertyporoch and Firla: Z. phys. Chem. **A 162**, 398 — 55, 57

**1933**

1. Evard: Bull. Soc. chim. Fr. (4) **53**, 1206 — 26
2. Backer and Keuning: Rec. Trav. chim. Pays-Bas **52**, 499 — 41

**1934**

1. Olmer and Quinet: Bull. Soc. chim. Fr. (5) **1**, 1579 — 18
2. Meerwein and Vossen: J. prakt. Chem. (2) **141**, 149 — 21, 22, 84
3. Meerwein and Pannwitz: J. prakt. Chem. (2) **141**, 123 — 21, 22, 48
4. Derner and Fernelius: Z. anorg. Chem. **221**, 83 — 26, 27, 43
5. Young: J. Amer. chem. Soc. **56**, 29 — 27, 81
6. Wertyporoch and Altmann: Z. phys. Chem. **A 168**, 1 — 34, 55
7. Wertyporoch and Silber: Z. phys. Chem. **A 168**, 124 — 55
8. Wertyporoch and Adamus: Z. phys. Chem. **A 168**, 31 — 55
9. Croxall, Sowa and Nieuwland: J. Amer. chem. Soc. **56**, 2054 — 86

**1935**

1. Martin, Pizzolato and McWaters: J. Amer. chem. Soc. **57**, 2584 — 83

**1936**

1. MacGillavry and Bijvoet: Z. Kristallogr., Mineralog., Petrogr. **94**, 249 — 5
2. MacGillavry and Bijvoet: Z. Kristallogr., Mineralog., Petrogr. **94**, 231 — 6
3. Kane and Lowy: J. Amer. chem. Soc. **58**, 2605 — 24, 84
4. Brass and Fanta: Ber. dtsch. chem. Ges. **69**, 1 — 25
5. Jensen and Rancke-Madsen: Z. anorg. Chem. **227**, 25 — 30
6. Luchinskii: Z. anorg. Chem. **226**, 333 — 44

**1937**

1. Klinkenberg: Rec. Trav. chim. Pays-Bas **56**, 749 — 14
2. Quinet: Bull. Soc. chim. Fr. (5) **4**, 518 — 18
3. Maki and Yokete: Chem. Abstr. **31**, 4499 — 35
4. Luchinskii: Chem. Abstr. **31**, 4613 — 43
5. Likhacheva: Chem. Abstr. **31**, 6127 — 44
6. Ewell: J. chem. Phys. **5**, 967 — 51
7. Jander and Immig: Z. anorg. Chem. **233**, 295 — 55
8. Fairbrother: J. chem. Soc. 503 — 84
9. McKenna and Sowa: J. Amer. chem. Soc. **59**, 1204 — 84
10. Toole and Sowa: J. Amer. chem. Soc. **59**, 1971 — 85

**1938**

1. Davidson and Chappell: J. Amer. chem. Soc. **60**, 2043 — 20
2. Krimberg: Biochem. Z. **297**, 261 — 21

3. Kurnakov and Voskresenskaya: Chem. Abstr. **32**, 2511 — 25, 32
4. Riebsomer, Baldwin, Buchanan and Burkett:
J. Amer. chem. Soc. **60**, 2974 — 25
5. Chretien and Oechsel: C. R. Acad. Sci. (Paris) **206**, 254 — 29
6. Likhacheva: Chem. Abstr. **32**, 443 — 45
7. Kurnakov and Shternin: C. **1938** I, 812 — 52
8. Klochko: Chem. Abstr. **32**, 2819 — 53
9. Kurnakov and Voskrensenskaya: C. **1938** I, 811 — 61

**1939**

1. Asmussen: Z. anorg. Chem. **243**, 127 — 14
2. Osokin: Chem. Abstr. **33**, 1263 — 17, 18
3. Chelintsev: Chem. Abstr. **33**, 1263 — 18
4. Pfeiffer and Blank: J. prakt. Chem. (2) **153**, 242 — 18
5. Brown, Schlessinger and Burg: J. Amer. chem. Soc. **61**, 673 — 21, 32, 82
6. Luchinskii: Chem. Abstr. **3**, 5312 — 44, 45

**1940**

1. Evans, Mann, Peiser and Purdie: J. chem. Soc. 1209 — 6, 7
2. Norris and Arthur: J. Amer. chem. Soc. **62**, 874 — 23, 81
3. Sachs and Ryffel-Neumann: J. Amer. chem. Soc. **62**, 993 — 26, 29
4. Davis and Green: J. Amer. chem. Soc. **62**, 1272 — 31
5. Hieber and Reindl: Z. Elektrochem. **46**, 559 — 61

**1941**

1. Ulich and Heyne: Z. phys. Chem. **B 49**, 284 — 32, 34, 78
2. Nizhnik: Chem. Abstr. **35**, 2798 — 55
3. Plotnikov and Vaisberg: Chem. Abstr. **35**, 2405 — 61
4. Sheka: Chem. Abstr. **35**, 2379 — 78

**1942**

1. Puschin, Nikolić, Radojčin and Voroponova:
Liebigs Ann. Chem. **551**, 259 — 34, 35
2. Hertel: Liebigs Ann. Chem. **553**, 286 — 35
3. Booth and Martin: J. Amer. chem. Soc. **64**, 2198 — 44
4. Luchinskii: Chem. Abstr. **36**, 2494 — 44
5. Gerding and Smit: Z. phys. Chem. **B 51**, 200 — 44

**1943**

1. Seel: Z. anorg. Chem. **250**, 331 — 32, 55, 84
2. Burg: J. Amer. chem. Soc. **65**, 1629 — 31
3. Booth and Walkup: J. Amer. chem. Soc. **65**, 2334 — 36, 41
4. Burg and Ross: J. Amer. chem. Soc. **65**, 1637 — 36, 59
5. Sheka: Chem. Abstr. **37**, 6538 — 78

**1944**

1. Wachsmuth: Chem. Abstr. **38**, 2340 — 13
2. Seel: Z. anorg. Chem. **252**, 24 — 14, 32, 55
3. Martin: Chem. Rev. **34**, 461 — 21
4. Heinänen: C. **1944** I, 345 — 25
5. Riley: J. Amer. chem. Soc. **66**, 512 — 35
6. Campbell and Eley: Nature (Lond.) **154**, 85 — 83

**1945**

1. Gerbault: C. R. Acad. Sci. (Paris) **221**, 51 — 19
2. Olmer and Gerbault: C. R. Acad. Sci. (Paris) **220**, 604 — 19
3. Marini-Bettòlo and Paoloni: Gazz. chim. ital. **75**, 78 — 20
4. Swisher: Chem. Abstr. **39**, 568 — 29
5. Burg and Dickerton: J. Amer. chem. Soc. **67**, 2261 — 33
6. Martin: J. Amer. chem. Soc. **67**, 1088 — 44
7. Bond and Belton: J. Amer. chem. Soc. **67**, 1691 — 44
8. Philips, Hunter and Sutton: J. chem. Soc. 146 — 92

**1946**

1. GERBAULT: C. R. Acad. Sci. (Paris) **222**, 1109 — 19
2. GERBAULT: C. R. Acad. Sci. (Paris) **222**, 292 — 31
3. VOSKRESENSKAYA, RAVICH and SHTERNINA: Chem. Abstr. **40**, 3047 — 51
4. TRIFONOV: Chem. Abstr. **40**, 3317 — 51
5. UDOVENKO: Chem. Abstr. **40**, 3334 — 51
6. KRASILNIKOV: Chem. Abstr. **40**, 4928 — 78

**1947**

1. LAPIÈRE: Analyt. chim. Acta (Amsterdam) **1**, 371 — 13
2. PROUT and CASON: J. Amer. chem. Soc. **69**, 1228 — 19
3. USANOVICH and KALABANOVSKAYA: Zhur. Obschei. Khim. **17**, 1235 — 25, 48, 52
4. FRICKE: Z. anorg. Chem. **253**, 173 — 34
5. HECHT: Z. anorg. Chem. **254**, 37 — 41
6. HECHT, JANDER and SCHLAPMANN: Z. anorg. Chem. **254**, 255 — 41, 42

**1948**

1. MARTIN: Chem. Rev. **42**, 581 — 21
2. LUKIN and ZAVARIKHINA: Chem. Abstr. **42**, 550 — 29
3. HOPFF: Angew. Chem. **60 A**, 245 — 32
4. BELOW and SAVICH: Chem. Abstr. **42**, 530 — 33
5. LECHER and HARDY: J. Amer. chem. Soc. **70**, 3789 — 33
6. PUSHIN, NIKOLIĆ, PARHOMENKO, RADOJČIN and VASOVIĆ: Chem. Abstr. **42**, 2201 — 35
7. PUSHIN: Zhur. Obschei. Khim. **18**, 1599 — 35
8. TOPSHIEV and PAUSHKIN: Chem. Abstr. **42**, 1182 — 36

**1949**

1. HARADA: Chem. Abstr. **43**, 7899 — 16
2. ESAFOV and NOVIKOV: Zhur. Obschei. Khim. **19**, 1344 — 18
3. MARINI-BETTÒLO and BARONI: Chem. Abstr. **43**, 7000 — 19
4. MARTIN and FAUST: J. phys. Colloid Chem. **53**, 1255 — 32
5. GRUEN and KATZ: J. Amer. chem. Soc. **71**, 3843 — 37
6. HAYEK and ENGELBRECHT: Mh. Chem. **80**, 640 — 44
7. DILKE and ELEY: J. chem. Soc. 2601 — 59, 60, 61, 62, 63, 85
8. DILKE and ELEY: J. chem. Soc. 2613 — 85
9. DIPPY and WOOD: J. chem. Soc. 2719 — 86

**1950**

1. GELLER and HOARD: Acta crystallogr. **3**, 121 — 7
2. HOARD, OWEN, BUZELL and SALMON: Acta crystallogr. **3**, 130 — 7
3. THEILACKER and LEICHTLE: Liebigs Ann. Chem. **572**, 121 — 19
4. THAKOR and SHAH: Chem. Abstr. **44**, 2473 — 19, 20
5. BRADLEY, ABD-EL HALIM and WARDLAW: J. chem. Soc. 3450 — 27, 60
6. DILKE, ELEY and SHEPPARD: Trans. Faraday Soc. **46**, 261 — 60, 108
7. MOFFITT: Proc. roy. Soc. **A 200**, 409 — 92

**1951**

1. HOARD, GELLER and CASHIN: Acta crystallogr. **4**, 396 — 7
2. GELLER and HOARD: Acta crystallogr. **4**, 399 — 7
3. HOARD, GELLER and OWEN: Acta crystallogr. **4**, 405 — 7
4. GOULD and MCCULLOUGH: J. Amer. chem. Soc. **73**, 3196 — 16, 45
5. HARADA: Chem. Abstr. **45**, 2356 — 16
6. SHINE: J. chem. Soc. 8 — 18
7. DIPPY and PALLUEL: J. chem. Soc. 1415 — 22
8. SUMAROKOVA and USANOVICH: Zhur. Obschei. Khim. **21**, 1219 — 28
9. USANOVICH and SUMAROKOVA: Zhur. Obschei. Khim. **21**, 1214 — 28
10. BURG and MCKEE: J. Amer. chem. Soc. **73**, 4590 — 36, 38
11. AYNSLEY, PEACOCK and ROBINSON: Chem. and Ind. 1117 — 45
12. VAN DYKE and CRAWFORD: J. Amer. chem. Soc. **73**, 2018 — 50, 54

13. Greenwood and Martin: J. chem. Soc. 1795 52, 53
14. Greenwood, Martin and Emeléus: J. chem. Soc. 1328 53, 54
15. Greenwood and Martin: Nature (Lond.) **168**, 344 52
16. Van Dyke: J. Amer. chem. Soc. **73**, 398 54
17. Lebedev: Zhur. Obschei. Khim. **21**, 1788 94

**1952**

1. Fuge, Bowden and Jones: J. phys. Chem. **56**, 1013 17
2. Lewis and Wright: J. Amer. chem. Soc. **74**, 1253 16, 18, 60
3. Dippy and Moss: J. chem. Soc. 2205 19, 26, 86
4. Greenwood and Martin: Proc. roy. Soc. **A 215**, 46 21, 52, 53
5. Cullinane, Chard and Leyshon: J. chem. Soc. 4106 26, 32
6. Bradley, Hancock and Wardlaw: J. chem. Soc. 2773 26
7. Bradley, Abd-el Halim, Mehrotra and Wardlaw: J. chem. Soc. 4609 27
8. Hummers, Tyree and Yolles: J. Amer. chem. Soc. **74**, 139 27, 61
9. Chapman, Hummers, Tyree and Yolles: J. Amer. chem. Soc. **74**, 5277 27, 81
10. Morgan and Herr: J. Amer. chem. Soc. **74**, 4526 35
11. Gutmann: Z. anorg. Chem. **269**, 279 36, 37, 38, 55
12. Larsen, Howatson, Gamill and Wittenberg: J. Amer. chem. Soc. **74**, 3489 37
13. Gutmann: Z. anorg. Chem. **270**, 179 49
14. Osipov and Suchkov: Zhur. Obschei. Khim. **22**, 1132 54
15. Spandau and Brunneck: Z. anorg. Chem. **270**, 201 55
16. Pray and McCrosky: J. Amer. chem. Soc. **74**, 4719 54
17. Hayek and Rhomberg: Mh. Chem. **83**, 1318 61, 81

**1953**

1. Struchkov, Kitaigorodskij and Khotsyanova: Dokl. Akad. Nauk SSSR, **93**, 675 6, 12, 20, 64
2. Gerding and Houtgraaf: Rec. Trav. chim. Pays-Bas **72**, 21 14
3. Greenwood and Martin: J. chem. Soc. 751 21, 52, 53, 54
4. Muetterties and Rochow: J. Amer. chem. Soc. **75**, 490 22
5. Coffey: Chem. and Ind. 1068 22, 23
6. Coates and Hayter: J. chem. Soc. 2519 24, 81
7. Wittig and Geissler: Liebigs Ann. Chem. **580**, 44 35
8. Groeneveld, van Spronsen and Kouwenhoven: Rec. Trav. chim. Pays-Bas **72**, 950 37
9. Baker and Sisler: J. Amer. chem. Soc. **75**, 5193 44
10. Greenwood and Martin: J. chem. Soc. 1427 53
11. Groeneveld and Zuur: Rec. Trav. chim. Pays-Bas **72**, 617 55
12. Miskidzhyan: Zhur. Obschei. Khim. **23**, 1947 58
13. Dehmelt: J. chem. Phys. **21**, 380 79

**1954**

1. Hassel and Hvoslef: Acta chem. scand. **8**, 1953 6
2. Cooke, Susz and Herschmann: Helv. chim. Acta **37**, 1280 12, 13, 23, 83
3. Susz and Cooke: Helv. chim. Acta **37**, 1273 12
4. Piper and Rochow: J. Amer. chem. Soc. **76**, 4318 12, 24
5. Pino and Ercoli: Chem. Abstr. **48**, 12106 21
6. Petrenko: Zhur. Obschei. Khim. **24**, 520 21, 31
7. Ruof and Howard: J. Amer. chem. Soc. **76**, 5565 26
8. Moore and Tyree: J. Amer. chem. Soc. **76**, 5253 27, 61, 81
9. Cozzi and Cecconi: Chem. Abstr. **48**, 3891 29
10. Utzinger and Regenass: Helv. chim. Acta **37**, 1892 33
11. Burg and Woodrow: J. Amer. chem. Soc. **76**, 219 41, 43
12. Osipov and Kravtsov: Chem. Abstr. **48**, 12534 52
13. Gutmann: Mh. Chem. **85**, 393 55
14. Gutmann and Lindqvist: Z. phys. Chem. **203**, 250 55
15. Gutmann: Mh. Chem. **85**, 404 55
16. Kuzmina and Volnov: Chem. Abstr. **48**, 8677 58

17. GORENBEIN: Zhur. Obschei. Khim. **24**, 1710 — 54
18. LYSENKO and OSIPOV: Zhur. Obschei. Khim. **24**, 53 — 61
19. BADDELEY and VOSS: J. chem. Soc. 418 — 84
20. CRAIG, MACCOLL, NYHOLM, ORGEL and SUTTON: J. chem. Soc. 332 — 92
21. BELL, HEISLER, TANNENBAUM and GOLDENSON: J. Amer. chem. Soc. **76**, 5185 — 93

**1955**

1. McBEE, PIERCE and MEYER: J. Amer. chem. Soc. **77**, 83 — 18
2. FRAZER and GERRARD: J. chem. Soc. 2959 — 21, 81
3. REPPE: Liebigs Ann. Chem. **596**, 158 — 21
4. VOLNOV, GLEZER and RAIKINA: Chem. Abstr. **49**, 6833 — 24, 25, 26, 81
5. TRIFONOV and FAIZULLIN: Chem. Abstr. **49**, 2167, 2168 — 27
6. SPANDAU and BRUNNECK: Z. anorg. Chem. **278**, 197 — 29, 55, 57
7. DADAPE and RAO: J. Amer. chem. Soc. **77**, 6192 — 39, 51
8. BACHMAN, FEUER, BLUESTEIN and VOGT: J. Amer. chem. Soc. **77**, 6188 — 44
9. OSIPOV and SEMENOV: Zhur. Obschei. Khim. **25**, 2059 — 50, 58
10. LARSEN and WITTENBERG: J. Amer. chem. Soc. **77**, 5850 — 50
11. OSIPOV, LYSENKO and AKAPOV: Zhur. Obschei. Khim. **25**, 249 — 52, 61
12. LINDQVIST: Acta chem. scand. **9**, 73 — 55
13. ANDERSSON and LINDQVIST: Acta chem. scand. **9**, 79 — 55
14. GUTMANN and HIMML: Z. phys. Chem. N. F. **4**, 157 — 57
15. LYSENKO, OSIPOV and FEODOSEV: Chem. Abstr. **49**, 5953 — 61
16. HALPERN, BOUCK, FINEGOLD and GOLDENSON: J. Amer. chem. Soc. **77**, 4472 — 63

**1956**

1. HASSEL and RÖMMING: Acta chem. scand. **10**, 136 — 6
2. GRDENIC and KRSTANOVIC: Chem. Abstr. **50**, 5361 — 6
3. ZVONKOVA: Kristallografiya **1**, 142 — 7
4. LEWIS and SOWERBY: Rec. Trav. chim. Pays-Bas **75**, 615 — 14
5. SARNOWSKI, ZYGADLO and SCIENSKA: Chem. Abstr. **50**, 8361 — 17
6. ESAFOV and NOVOKOV: Zhur. Obschei. Khim. **26**, 2758 — 18
7. SARNOWSKI, BARANOWSKI and ZYGADLO: Chem. Abstr. **50**, 6878 — 18
8. GERRARD and WHEELANS: J. chem. Soc. 4296 — 21, 81
9. BECHER: Ber. dtsch. chem. Ges. **89**, 1691 — 22
10. OSIPOV: Zhur. Obschei. Khim. **26**, 322 — 25, 26, 78
11. SUMAROKOVA and YARMUKHAMEDOVA: Zhur. Obschei. Khim. **26**, 3295 — 25
12. YOSHINO, KIJIMA and HASHIMURA: Chem. Abstr. **50**, 3294 — 26
13. LYSENKO, OSIPOV and AKOPOV: Zhur. Neorg. Khim. **1**, 536 — 26
14. KAPUSTINSKII and SOLOKHIN: Chem. Abstr. **50**, 9849 — 30, 63
15. OLÁH and KUHN: Ber. dtsch. chem. Ges. **89**, 866 — 32
16. GREENWOOD and WADE: J. chem. Soc. 1527 — 32, 55, 60, 84
17. BROWN and HOLMES: J. Amer. chem. Soc. **78**, 2173 — 34, 108
18. PAYNE: Rec. Trav. chim. Pays-Bas **75**, 620 — 36, 37, 54, 61
19. GUTMANN and HIMML: Z. anorg. Chem. **287**, 199 — 37, 41, 45, 46, 49, 55
20. SHEKA and VOITOVICH: Zhur. Neorg. Khim. **1**, 964 — 37
21. NISELSON and IVANOV-EMIN: Zhur. Neorg. Khim. **1**, 1766 — 37
22. NISELSON: Zhur. Neorg. Khim. **1**, 657 — 37
23. KLAGES and ZANGE: Angew. Chem. **68**, 704 — 47
24. KLAGES, MÜHLBAUER and UHL: Angew. Chem. **68**, 704 — 47
25. SUMAROKOVA and LITVYAK: Chem. Abstr. **50**, 16526 — 48
26. SUMAROKOVA and MAKSAI: Chem. Abstr. **50**, 16526 — 48
27. LEVITT and FREUND: J. Amer. chem. Soc. **78**, 1545 — 51
28. LYSENKO: Zhur. Obschei. Khim. **26**, 2963 — 52
29. LYSENKO: Zhur. Obschei. Khim. **26**, 3273 — 52
30. MASTERS, POTTER, ASHER and NORRIS: J. Amer. chem. Soc. **78**, 4252 — 57
31. SHEKA: Zhur. Obschei. Khim. **26**, 1340 — 79
32. CULLINANE, EVANS and LLOYD: J. chem. Soc. 2222 — 85
33. CUMPER and WALKER: Trans. Faraday Soc. **52**, 193 — 92
34. MULLER, LAUTERBEER and GOLDENSON: J. Amer. chem. Soc. **78**, 3557 — 92
35. LINDQVIST and NIGGLI: J. inorg. nucl. Chem. **2**, 345 — 107

36. STROHMEIER: Z. Elektrochem. **60**, 58 108
37. STROHMEIER and HÜMPFNER: Z. Elektrochem. **60**, 1111 108

**1957**

1. NARDELLI, CAVALCA and FAVA: Gazz. chim. ital. **87**, 1232 6, 12
2. MALINOVSKIJ: Kristallografiya **2**, 734 9, 99
3. DUNITZ: Acta crystallogr. **10**, 307 9
4. VUAGNAT and SUSZ: Chem. Abstr. **51**, 5556 11
5. CHALANDON and SUSZ: Chem. Abstr. **51**, 10237 12
6. CAVALCA, NARDELLI and COGHI: Nuovo Cimento **6**, 278 12
7. PENLAND, MIZUSHIMA, CURRAN and QUAGLIANO: J. Amer. chem. Soc. **79**, 1575 12, 19, 31
8. SUSZ and WUHRMANN: Helv. chim. Acta **40**, 971 13, 32
9. SUSZ and WUHRMANN: Helv. chim. Acta **40**, 722 13, 32
10. GROSSMAN: J. org. Chem. **22**, 581 14, 34, 35
11. LEWIS and SOWERBY: J. chem. Soc. 1617 14
12. NARDELLI, BRABIANTI and CHIERICI: Gazz. chim. ital. **87**, 1226 19, 20, 21
13. LOMBARD and STÉPHAN: Bull. Soc. chim. Fr. 1369 21, 82
14. FRAZER, GERRARD and LAPPERT: J. chem. Soc. 739 21, 82
15. TOPCHIEV and ANDRONOV: Chem. Abstr. **51**, 11981 36
16. GROENEVELD and ZUUR: Rec. Trav. chim. Pays-Bas **76**, 1005 36
17. GREENWOOD and WADE: J. chem. Soc. 1516 36, 52, 53
18. GREENWOOD and PERKINS: J. inorg. nucl. Chem. **4**, 291 36, 61
19. BRADLEY, CHAKRAVARTI and CHATTERJEE: J. inorg. nucl. Chem. **3**, 367 42
20. BACHMANN and HOKAMA: J. Amer. chem. Soc. **79**, 4371 44
21. SUMAROKOVA and LITVYAK: Zhur. Obschei. Khim. **27**, 837 48, 52
22. SUMAROKOVA and LITVYAK: Zhur. Obschei. Khim. **27**, 1125 48
23. OSIPOV, SAMOFALOVA and GLUSHKO: Zhur. Obschei. Khim. **27**, 1428 48, 78
24. UDOVENKO and FIALKOV: Zhur. Neorg. Khim. **2**, 868 52
25. UDOVENKO and FIALKOV: Zhur. Neorg. Khim. **2**, 434 52
26. GUTMANN and TANNENBERGER: Mh. Chem. **88**, 292 55
27. GUTMANN and TANNENBERGER: Mh. Chem. **88**, 216 55, 56
28. GUTMANN and MAIRINGER: Z. anorg. Chem. **289**, 279 55
29. LEWIS and SOWERBY: Chem. Soc. Spec. Publ. **10**, 123 57
30. USANOVICH, KLIMOV and SUMAROKOVA: Chem. Abstr. **51**, 11887 58
31. OSIPOV and KLETENIK: Zhur. Obschei. Khim. **27**, 2921 78
32. NISELSON: Zhur. Neorg. Khim. **2**, 816 38
33. HAHN: Z. Krist. **109**, 4 91

**1958**

1. SCHULTZ and PARRY: J. Amer. chem. Soc. **80**, 4 2
2. TAYLOR, SCHULTZ and EMERY: J. Amer. chem. Soc. **80**, 27 2
3. AGERMAN, ANDERSSON, LINDQVIST and ZACKRISSON: Acta chem. scand. **12**, 477 8, 36, 37, 38, 45, 46
4. TERENIN, FILIMONOV and BYSTROV: Z. Elektrochem. **62**, 180 11, 12, 14, 64
5. COERVER and CURRAN: J. Amer. chem. Soc. **80**, 3522 11
6. SUSZ and CHALANDON: Helv. chim. Acta **41**, 1332 11, 12, 19, 21, 22, 63
7. CHALANDON and SUSZ: Helv. chim. Acta **41**, 697 12, 21, 64, 78
8. SUSZ and LACHAVANNE: Helv. chim. Acta **41**, 634 12
9. AUBIN and RIVEST: Canad. J. Chem. **36**, 915 12, 26
10. NARDELLI, COGHI and AZZONI: Gazz. chim. ital. 88, 235 12
11. ARCHAMBAULT and RIVEST: Canad. J. Chem. **36**, 1461 12, 27, 65
12. SHELDON and TYREE: J. Amer. chem. Soc. **80**, 4775 13, 15, 16, 36, 37, 39, 68, 69
13. GAGNAUX, JANJIC and SUSZ: Helv. chim. Acta **41**, 1023 14, 78
14. GAGNAUX, JANJIC and SUSZ: Helv. chim. Acta **41**, 1322 14, 34
15. SARNOWSKI and BARANOWSKI: Chem. Abstr. **52**, 19373 17
16. SARNOWSKI, SCIENSKA and ZYGADLO: Chem. Abstr. **52**, 19373 e 17, 19
17. SARNOWSKI, SCIENSKA and ZYGADLO: Chem. Abstr. **52**, 19373 g 17, 18
18. NARDELLI, CAVALCA and COGHI: Chem. Abstr. **52**, 13510 20
19. NARDELLI and COGHI: Chem. Abstr. **52**, 12505 20

20. GREENWOOD: J. inorg. nucl. Chem. 8, 234 61
21. YARMUKHAMEDOVA and SUMAROKOVA: Zhur. Obschei. Khim. 28, 1410 24, 26
22. EMELÉUS and RAO: J. chem. Soc. 4245 26, 32, 34
23. LYSENKO and OSIPOV: Zhur. Obschei. Khim. 28, 1724 26, 81
24. CHKHENKELI: Chem. Abstr. **52**, 16848 30
25. KOTELNIKOVA and TRONEV: Zhur. Neorg. Khim. **3**, 1008 30
26. FUNK and KÖHLER: Z. anorg. Chem. **294**, 233 31
27. GROENEVELD and ZUUR: J. inorg. nucl. Chem. 8, 241 36
28. GREENWOOD and WORRALL: J. inorg. nucl. Chem. **6**, 34 36, 52, 53
29. SHEKA and VOITOVICH: Zhur. Neorg. Khim. **3**, 1973 37
30. KRETOV: Chem. Abstr. **52**, 4550 43
31. BACHMAN and DEVER: J. Amer. chem. Soc. 80, 5871 44
32. GUTMANN and MAIRINGER: Mh. Chem. **89**, 724 49, 55
33. VOLNOV: Chem. Abstr. **52**, 8691 49
34. GRAUTIER: C. R. Acad. Sci. (Paris) **247**, 2139 54
35. PAUL, SINGH and SANDHU: Chem. and Ind. 622 55
36. LINDQVIST: Acta chem. scand. **12**, 135 56
37. KLIMOV, USANOVICH and SUMAROKOVA: Chem. Abstr. **52**, 6022 58
38. KLIMOV, USANOVICH and SUMAROKOVA: Chem. Abstr. **52**, 19300 58
39. ALLEN and WARHURST: Trans. Faraday Soc. **54**, 1786 65
40. GERRARD and LAPPERT: Chem. Rev. **58**, 1081 82
41. BROWN and JENSEN: J. Amer. chem. Soc. **80**, 2291 83
42. JENSEN and BROWN: J. Amer. chem. Soc. **80**, 3039 83
43. COOK: J. Amer. chem. Soc. **80**, 49 91
44. GILLIS, HORWOOD and WHITE: J. Amer. chem. Soc. **80**, 2999 92
45. BALIAH and SHANMUGANATHAN: J. phys. Chem. **62**, 255 92
46. FYFE: J. chem. Phys. **28**, 907 106
47. STONE: Chem. Rev. **58**, 101 107, 108
48. AHRLAND, CHATT and DAVIES: Quart. Revs. (London) **12**, 265 109

**1959**

1. FERRARO: J. inorg. nucl. Chem. **10**, 319 7, 9
2. BREDERECK, GOMPPER, KLEMM and REMPFER: Ber. dtsch. chem. Ges. **92**, 837 8
3. LINDQVIST and BRÄNDÉN: Acta crystallogr. **12**, 642 8, 15
4. LINDQVIST and NAHRINGBAUER: Acta crystallogr. **12**, 638 9
5. PAOLONI and MARINI-BETTÒLO: Gazz. chim. ital. **89**, 1972 11, 12, 19, 20, 64
6. PAOLONI: Gazz. chim. ital. **89**, 2171 12
7. GOMPPER and ALTREUTHER: Z. analyt. Chem. **170**, 205 12, 22
8. MARTINETTE, MIZUSHIMA and QUAGLIANO: Spectrochim. Acta **77** 12
9. COOK: Canad. J. Chem. **37**, 48 13
10. SHELDON and TYREE: J. Amer. chem. Soc. **81**, 2290 13, 15, 16, 32, 37, 41, 45, 68, 76
11. LINDQVIST and OLOFSSON: Acta chem. scand. **13**, 1753 15, 35, 37, 38, 69
12. KINELL, LINDQVIST and ZACKRISSON: Acta chem. scand. **13**, 1159 15, 67, 68, 69, 78
13. GUT and SCHWARZENBACH: Helv. chim. Acta **42**, 2156 15, 38, 68
14. PRASAD and SRIVASTAVA: Chem. Abstr. **53**, 13861 17
15. PAUL, SINGH and SANDHU: J. chem. Soc. 319 19, 29, 30
16. FIALKOV: Shurn. Obsch. Chimii. **29**, 1442 24, 55
17. DIANOV and TRIFONOV: Chem. Abstr. **53**, 7745 25
18. JOSEPH and BLUMENTHAL: J. org. Chem. **24**, 1371 27, 81
19. KLETENIK, OSIPOV and KRAVTSOV: Zhur. Obschei. Khim. **29**, 11 27, 50, 78
20. KLETENIK and OSIPOV: Zhur. Obschei. Khim. **29**, 1423 27, 50, 59, 79
21. KLAGES, TRÄGER and MÜHLBAUER: Ber. dtsch. chem. Ges. **92**, 1819 28
22. KLAGES and ZANGE: Ber. dtsch. chem. Ges. **92**, 1828 28, 47
23. FUNK, MOHAUPT and PAUL: Z. anorg. Chem. **302**, 199 29
24. DEICH and NASONOV: Zhur. Neorg. Khim. **4**, 1198 30
25. FREEMAN, SMITH and TAYLOR: Nature (Lond.) **184**, 707 31
26. GUTMANN and UTVARY: Mh. Chem. **90**, 751 32, 33, 55
27. PAUL, SINGH and SANDHU: J. chem. Soc. 315 32

28. PAUL, BAINS and SINGH: Chem. Abstr. **53**, 7724 33
29. WANNAGAT and PFEIFFENSCHNEIDER: Z. anorg. Chem. **297**, 151 33
30. GORENBEIN and DANILOVA: Chem. Abstr. **53**, 16657 34, 50
31. GREENWOOD and THOMPSON: J. chem. Soc. 3493 36, 53, 54
32. ISSLEIB and BOHN: Z. anorg. Chem. **301**, 188 36, 38
33. VENKATARAMAN and VASUDEVAMURTHY: Chem. Abstr. **53**, 10905 36
34. GUTMANN and BAAZ: Mh. Chem. **90**, 729 36, 39, 56
35. LINDQVIST, ZACKRISSON and ERIKSSON: Acta chem. scand. **13**, 1758 36, 37
36. LEMAN and TRIDOT: C. R. Acad. Sci. (Paris) **248**, 3439 37
37. LINDQVIST and EINARSSON: Acta chem. scand. **13**, 420 37, 42, 43
38. SHEKA, VOITOVICH and NISELSON: Zhur. Neorg. Khim. **4**, 1803 38
39. GUTMANN and UTVARY: Mh. Chem. **90**, 706 41
40. USANOVICH and DEMBITSKII: Zhur. Obschei. Khim. **29**, 1771, 1781 49
41. OSIPOV and KLETENIK: Zhur. Obschei. Khim. **29**, 1375 50, 51, 59
42. OSIPOV and KLETENIK: Zhur. Obschei. Khim. **29**, 2119 50, 59, 79
43. RABINOVICH and PONOMAVENKO: Chem. Abstr. **53**, 11954 50
44. VOLNOV: Zhur. Neorg. Khim. **4**, 2287 50
45. IRVING and EDGINGTON: J. inorg. nucl. Chem. **10**, 306 51
46. SUMAROKOVA, OMAROVA and KUZMENKO: Zhur. Obschei. Khim. **29**, 1437 52, 58
47. MANHAS, PAUL and SANDHU: J. chem. Soc. 325 55
48. KLIKORKA and PAVLÍK: Chem. Abstr. **53**, 5827 55
49. KLIKORKA and PAVLÍK: Collect. czechoslov. chem. Commun. **24**, 2516 55
50. PAUL, SINGH and SANDHU: Analyt. Chem. **31**, 1495 55
51. HARRIS: Chem. Abstr. **53**, 4966 58
52. SUMAROKOVA and OMAROVA: Zhur. Obschei. Khim. **29**, 1430 58
53. GUTMANN and BAAZ: Z. anorg. Chem. **298**, 121 56
54. BAAZ and GUTMANN: Mh. Chem. **90**, 256, 276, 744 58
55. KINELL, LINDQVIST and ZACKRISSON: Acta chem. scand. **13**, 190 59
56. GORENBEIN: Zhur. Neorg. Khim. **4**, 1643 59
57. SUSZ: C. R. Acad. Sci. (Paris) **248**, 2569 63
58. JENSEN, MARINO and BROWN: J. Amer. chem. Soc. **81**, 3303 83
59. COTTON and LETO: J. chem. Phys. **30**, 993 97, 108
60. BREHLER: Naturwissenschaften **46**, 106, 554 5, 99
61. HASSEL and STRÖMME: Acta chem. scand. **13**, 275 10

**1960**

1. BRÄNDÉN and LINDQVIST: Acta chem. scand. **14**, 726 3, 8, 15, 37, 66
2. OLOVSSON: Acta chem. scand. **14**, 1453 4
3. CAVALCA, NARDELLI and BRANCHI: Acta crystallogr. **13**, 688 5, 31
4. BREHLER: Z. Krist. **114**, 66 5
5. ORGEL: An introduction to transition metal chemistry. Methuen, London 1960 5, 9
6. BANNISTER and COTTON: J. chem. Soc. 1878 5, 10
7. CAVALCA, NARDELLI and FAVA: Acta crystallogr. **13**, 594 3, 6, 12, 20, 99
8. HULME, LEIGH and BEATTIE: J. chem. Soc. 366 8
9. HERMODSSON: Acta crystallogr. **13**, 656 8, 16, 74
10. FLEMING and LYNTON: Chem. and Ind. 1415 9, 38
11. BANNISTER and COTTON: J. chem. Soc. 2276 10, 15, 35, 39
12. ISSLEIB and MITSCHERLING: Z. anorg. Chem. **304**, 73 10, 39, 79
13. HOLM and COTTON: J. chem. Phys. **32**, 1168 10
14. COTTON and GOODGAME: J. Amer. chem. Soc. **82**, 5771 10, 15, 39, 69
15. GOODGAME and COTTON: J. Amer. chem. Soc. **82**, 5774 10, 40, 67
16. COTTON and FRANCIS: J. Amer. chem. Soc. **82**, 2986 10, 15, 40, 41, 42
17. MEEK, STRAUB and DRAGO: J. Amer. chem. Soc. **82**, 6013 10, 15, 40, 42
18. CASSIMATIS and SUSZ: Helv. chim. Acta **43**, 852 11, 12
19. COTTON, BARNES and BANNISTER: J. chem. Soc. 2199 11, 15, 35, 39
20. GERRARD, LAPPERT, PYSZORA and WALLIS: J. chem. Soc. 2182 11
21. YAMDA: Chem. Abstr. **54**, 23626 11
22. PESTEMER and LAUERER: Angew. Chem. **76**, 612 12, 13

23. ZACKRISSON and ALDÉN:
Acta chem. scand. **14**, 994 — 12, 15, 27, 28, 38, 63, 64, 68, 69
24. BYSTROV and FILIMONOV: Dokl. Akad. Nauk, SSSR, **131**, 338 — 12, 64
25. COOK: Canad. J. Chem. **38**, 2143 — 12, 18
26. GERRARD, LAPPERT, PYSZORA and WALLIS: J. chem. Soc. 2144 — 12, 65, 80
27. ARCHAMBAULD and RIVEST: Canad. J. Chem. **38**, 1331 — 12, 27, 65
28. MUETTERTIES: J. Amer. chem. Soc. **82**, 1082 — 12, 24, 26, 27, 28, 41, 42, 80
29. CASSIMATIS, GAGNAUX and SUSZ: Helv. chim. Acta **43**, 424 — 13, 32
30. COOK, KUHN and OLÁH: J. chem. Phys. **33**, 1669 — 14
31. FRAZER, GERRARD and PATEL: J. chem. Soc. 726 — 15, 36
32. GERDING, KONINGSTEIN and VAN DER WORM: Spectrochim. Acta **16**, 881 — 15
33. WADDINGTON and KLANBERG: J. chem. Soc. 2339 — 15, 36
34. COTTON, FRANCIS and HORROCKS: J. phys. Chem. **64**, 1534 — 15, 73
35. NARDELLI and COGHI: Chem. Abstr. **54**, 1151 — 19, 20, 30, 31
36. LINDQVIST and ROSENSTEIN: Acta chem. scand. **14**, 1228 — 21
37. GERRARD, LAPPERT and WALLIS: J. chem. Soc. 2141 — 22, 27, 81
38. GREENWOOD and PERKINS: J. chem. Soc. 356 — 24, 60, 61
39. SUMAROKOVA, NEVSKAYA and YARMUKHAMEDOVA: Zhur. Obschei. Khim. **30**, 1705 — 24, 26, 28, 50
40. CSUROS, DEAK and FENICHEL: Chem. Abstr. **54**, 13931 — 26
41. EHRLICH and SIEBERT: Z. anorg. Chem. **303**, 96 — 26, 27
42. KLOCHKO and GUBSKAYA: Zhur. Neorg. Khim. **5**, 2491 — 31
43. BAAZ, GUTMANN and HÜBNER: Mh. Chem. **91**, 694 — 36, 55, 56
44. HOLMES: J. inorg. nucl. Chem. **12**, 266 — 36
45. PANZER and SUTTLE: J. inorg. nucl. Chem. **15**, 67 — 38
46. LAUGHLIN: J. org. Chem. **25**, 864 — 41, 43
47. SCHLÄFER and SCHAFFERNICHT: Angew. Chem. **72**, 618 — 42, 92
48. SUMAROKOVA, MEDVEDEVA and LITVYAK: Zhur. Obschei. Khim. **30**, 1698 — 48
49. ADOLFSSON, BRYNTSE and LINDQVIST: Acta chem. scand. **14**, 949 — 48, 49
50. VOITOVICH: Zhur. Neorg. Khim. **5**, 1981 — 50, 59
51. SOLOVKIN, KONAREV and ADAEV: Zhur. Neorg. Khim. **5**, 1861 — 51
52. SIDDALL: J. phys. Chem. **64**, 1863 — 51
53. BAAZ, GUTMANN and HÜBNER: Mh. Chem. **91**, 537 — 55
54. BAAZ, GUTMANN and TALAAT: Mh. Chem. **91**, 548 — 55
55. GUTMANN and BAAZ: Electrochim. Acta **3**, 115 — 58
56. LINDQVIST and ZACKRISSON: Acta chem. scand. **14**, 453 — 61, 62
57. LINDQVIST and FJELLSTRÖM: Acta chem. scand. **14**, 2055 — 61, 62
58. OSIPOV and LYSENKO: Zhur. Neorg. Khim. **5**, 1840 — 61
59. OSIPOV and KLETENIK: Zhur. Neorg. Khim. **5**, 2220 — 61
60. OSIPOV and LYSENKO: Zhur. Obschei. Khim. **30**, 3866 — 78
61. BUCK, BLOEMHOFF and OESTERHOFF: Tetrahedron Letters **9**, 5 — 80
62. ISSLEIB and TZSCHACH: Z. anorg. Chem. **305**, 198 — 82
63. LINDQVIST: Nova Acta Regiae Soc. Sci.
Upsaliensis (4) **17**, No. 11 — 89, 93, 94, 97, 99, 101
64. HERBER: J. Amer. chem. Soc. **82**, 792 — 57
65. LINDQVIST: Acta chem. scand. **14**, 1112 — 101

**1961**

1. KOLDITZ and PREISS: Z. anorg. Chem. **310**, 242 — 2
2. BRÄNDÉN and LINDQVIST: Acta chem. scand. **15**, 167 — 8, 15
3. GOODGAME and COTTON: J. chem Soc. 3735 — 10, 15, 38, 40
4. GOODGAME and COTTON: J. chem Soc. 2298 — 10, 15, 39, 40
5. SELBIN, BULL and HOLMES: J. inorg. nucl. Chem. **16**, 219 — 10, 15, 40, 41, 42, 73
6. GUTMANN and HÜBNER: Mh. Chem. **92**, 1261 — 10
7. LAPPERT: J. chem. Soc. 817 — 11, 12, 21, 23, 24, 25, 26, 30, 64, 79
8. COOK: Canad. J. Chem. **39**, 1184 — 11, 12, 19, 20, 21, 28
9. ZACKRISSON and LINDQVIST: J. inorg. nucl. Chem. **17**, 69 — 12, 25, 28, 64
10. BYSTROV, SUMAROKOVA and FILIMONOV: Chem. Abstr. **55**, 13055 — 12, 26
11. SUSZ and CASSIMATIS: Helv. chim. Acta **44**, 395 — 13, 32
12. CASSIMATIS and SUSZ: Helv. chim. Acta **44**, 943 — 13, 32

13. Quagliano, Fujita, Franz, Phillips, Walmsley and Tyree: J. Amer. chem. Soc. **83**, 3770 — 14, 33, 34
14. Gagnaux and Susz: Helv. chim. Acta **44**, 1132 — 14, 34
15. Gerrard, Mooney and Willis: J. chem. Soc. 4255 — 15
16. Phillips and Tyree: J. Amer. chem. Soc. **83**, 1806 — 15, 39, 40
17. Bittrich, Gaube and Landsberg: J. prakt. Chem. (4) **12**, 198 — 18
18. Massey: J. chem. Soc. 1103 — 21
19. Kempa and Lee: Z. anorg. Chem. **311**, 140 — 25, 26
20. Pande and Misra: J. prakt. Chem. (4) **14**, 164 — 30, 54
21. Gagnaux and Susz: Helv. chim. Acta **44**, 1128 — 34
22. Wiberg and Müller-Schiedmayer: Z. anorg. Chem. **308**, 352 — 36
23. Dehnicke: Z. anorg. Chem. **308**, 72 — 36
24. Becke-Goehring and Thielemann: Z. anorg. Chem. **308**, 33 — 38, 39, 40
25. Sheldon: J. chem. Soc. 750 — 38, 40, 47
26. Danielsen and Rasmussen: Acta chem. scand. **15**, 1398 — 38
27. Goodgame, Goodgame and Cotton: J. Amer. chem. Soc. **83**, 4161 — 39, 40
28. Lappert and Smith: J. chem. Soc. 3224 — 15, 40, 41, 73, 82
29. Schläfer and Opitz: Z. anorg. Chem. **313**, 178 — 42
30. Frazer: J. chem. Soc. 3165 — 45
31. Gutmann and Mairinger: Mh. Chem. **92**, 720 — 49
32. Baaz, Gutmann, Hübner, Mairinger and West: Z. anorg. Chem. **311**, 302 — 49, 55
33. Meek and Drago: J. Amer. chem. Soc. **83**, 4322 — 55
34. Baaz, Gutmann and West: Mh. Chem. **92**, 164 — 55, 56
35. Baaz, Gutmann, Talaat and West: Mh. Chem. **92**, 150 — 55, 56
36. Sandhu, Datta and Paul: Chem. Abstr. **55**, 73 — 55
37. Baaz, Gutmann and Masaguer: Mh. Chem. **92**, 590 — 55, 56, 110
38. Baaz, Gutmann and Masaguer: Mh. Chem. **92**, 582 — 55
39. Baaz, Gutmann and Hübner: Mh. Chem. **92**, 135 — 55
40. Baaz, Gutmann and Talaat: Mh. Chem. **92**, 714 — 55
41. Gutmann and Hampel: Mh. Chem. **92**, 1048 — 56, 110
42. Baaz, Gutmann and Hübner: Mh. Chem. **92**, 272 — 56, 110
43. Moodie: Chem. and Ind. 1269 — 59
44. Zackrisson: Acta chem. scand. **15**, 1785 — 61, 62
45. Zackrisson: Acta chem. scand. **15**, 1784 — 61, 62
46. Sumarokova, Litvyak and Valezhanina: Chem. Abstr. **55**, 8021 — 64
47. Osipov: Chem. Abstr. **55**, 22973 — 79
48. Frazer, Gerrard and Singh: J. chem. Soc. 4680 — 81
49. Oulevey and Susz: Helv. chim. Acta **94**, 1425 — 84
50. Bent: J. inorg. nucl. Chem. **19**, 43 — 89, 93, 94
51. Cook: Canad. J. Chem. **39**, 31 — 91
52. Cruickshank: J. chem. Soc. 5486 — 92, 97, 106
53. Markov, Voitovich and Barbanova: Zhur. Neorg. Khim. **6**, 1204 — 36, 37
54. Machle and O'Hare: Trans. Faraday Soc. **57**, 2119 — 103
55. Rivet, Aubin and Rivest: Canad. J. Chem. **39**, 2343 — 12, 25, 26, 27

**1962**

1. Lindqvist and Sandmark: private communication — 5
2. Strandberg and Svensson: private communication — 5
3. Strandberg, Åkerby and Biddle: private communication — 5
4. Brändén: Acta chem. scand. (in the press) — 7, 69
5. Brändén: private communication — 7
6. Eriks: preliminary communication — 7, 15, 71
7. Brändén: Acta chem. scand. (in the press) — 8, 15, 66
8. Hansson and Brunge: private communication — 8, 15, 72
9. Hansson and Vänngård: private communication — 8, 15, 72
10. Hansson: private communication — 8, 16, 73
11. Brändén, Brun and Lindqvist: preliminary communication — 8, 12, 29, 65
12. Hermodsson: private communication — 8, 16, 74
13. Brändén and Lindqvist: Acta chem. scand. (in the press) — 8, 15, 66
14. Vänngård: private communication — 8, 69

15. WARTENBURG: Proc. 7 ICCC, 214 — 15, 36, 69
16. ISSLEIB and KREIBICH: Z. anorg. Chem. **313**, 338 — 10, 33, 34
17. JELLINEK: Proc. 7 ICCC, 230 — 37
18. HANSSON: private communication — 43
19. MORI, GÖHRING, CASSIMATIS and SUSZ: Helv. chim. Acta **45**, 77 — 12, 26, 64, 85
20. OLOFSSON, LINDQVIST and SUNNER: Acta chem. scand. (in the press) — 62
21. HORNER and TYREE: Inorg. Chem. **1**, 122 — 12, 14, 15, 33, 38, 40, 42
22. LANGFORD and LANGFORD: Inorg. Chem. **1**, 184 — 43
23. LÖWDIN: private communication — 89
24. LOCK and WILKINSON: Chem. and Ind. **40**, — 38, 40
25. LAPPERT: J. chem. Soc. 542 — 24, 26, 27, 65
26. HITCHCOOK and ELVING: Proc. 7 ICCC, 226 — 24, 79
27. PAOLONI: Proc. 7 ICCC, 212 — 64
28. ZEIL: Proc. 7 ICCC, 215 — 98
29. HASSEL and RÖMMING: Quart. Revs. (London) **16**, 1 — 10
30. ISSLEIB and RHEINHOLD: Z. anorg. Chem. **314**, 113 — 36
31. LINDQVIST aud FJELLSTRÖM: preliminary communication — 36, 43
32. BRÄNDÉN, HANSSON, HERMODSSON and LINDQVIST. Z. Krist. (in the press) — 76